Hello, Hilary.
Come in and Have a Seat."

The voice from the darkness nearly scared her out of her wits. But without a doubt she knew who it was.

"Logan!" she said in a muted voice. "What are you doing in my home?"

Flipping on the light she only succeeded in throwing his frame into shadowy relief. Slowly he rose and approached her.

"I came to see you because we need to reach an understanding." Abruptly he grabbed her in a crushing embrace that clearly revealed his desire.

"You'll be marrying me, Hilary Forrester. And while I don't care about past romances, there won't be more. I don't share my holdings with any man. So tell your artist friend to get another bedmate."

STEPHANIE JAMES
readily admits that the chief influence on her writing is her "life-long addiction to romantic daydreaming." She dislikes unhappy endings and always reads the last page of a book first to make certain it ends properly. *A Passionate Business* is her first Silhouette Romance.

Dear Reader:

At Silhouette we try to publish books with you, our reader, in mind, and we're always trying to think of something new. We're very pleased to announce the creation of Silhouette First Love, a new line of contemporary romances written by the very finest young adult writers especially for our twelve-to-sixteen-year-old readers. First Love has many of the same elements you've enjoyed in Silhouette Romances—love stories, happy endings and the same attention to detail and description—but features heroines and situations with which our younger readers can more easily identify.

First Love from Silhouette will be available in bookstores this October. We will introduce First Love with six books, and each month thereafter we'll bring you two new First Love romances.

We welcome any suggestions or comments, and I invite you to write to us at the address below.

Karen Solem
Editor-in-Chief
Silhouette Books
P. O. Box 769
New York, N.Y. 10019

STEPHANIE JAMES
A Passionate Business

Silhouette *Romance*

Published by Silhouette Books New York

America's Publisher of Contemporary Romance

Other Silhouette Books by Stephanie James

Dangerous Magic
Corporate Affair
Stormy Challenge

SILHOUETTE BOOKS, a Simon & Schuster Division
GULF & WESTERN CORPORATION
1230 Avenue of the Americas, New York, N.Y. 1002

Copyright © 1981 by Stephanie James

Distributed by Pocket Books

ISBN: 0-671-47444-8

First Silhouette printing July, 1981

10 9 8 7 6 5 4 3

America's Publisher of Contemporary Romance

Printed in the U.S.A.

Chapter One

"You may tell Mr. Saber that his future wife is waiting to see him," Hilary Forrester announced with fine hauteur. "You may also add that she hasn't appreciated being kept waiting for nearly an hour!"

The lie had the expected devastating impact on the pleasant, competent-looking woman who sat behind the desk in Logan Saber's outer office. Her name, according to the little sign in front of her, was E. Morgan and she appeared to be somewhere in her early thirties, married if the ring was any indication and possibly the mother of two. This last assumption was based on the presence of two framed photographs of laughing children who had E. Morgan's eyes. Even without all the clues, Hilary thought she would have guessed the secretary's background. E. Morgan had that married-with-kids look and that surprised Hilary. She would have expected a more flamboyant sort of female to be occupying the desk.

"His wife!" E. Morgan exclaimed, obviously quite startled.

"His *future* wife," Hilary corrected sweetly, well aware that the other woman had every right to be shocked by her claim. After all, it was a safe bet that Logan Saber's women, and there were undoubtedly several of them, bore little or no resemblance to herself. A man like Saber would almost certainly be seen with glamorously exciting, chic creatures. They wouldn't have honey-brown hair like Hilary; they would be blonde. And they wouldn't wear said hair in a heavy braid wound around the head in a neat, old-fashioned coronet as Hilary habitually did. Blonde hair was usually worn in deceptively casual, windswept styles here in Southern California.

Hilary was quite certain she didn't run true to type in a number of other ways. Her figure could be described as slender, but she was not blessed with either a model's slimness or the voluptuousness of a starlet. A pair of long-lashed amber eyes were probably the best feature of an otherwise attractive but not beautiful face. The face, with its rather firm little chin, a mouth that smiled readily and the candid, straightforward expression in the amber eyes, was not made up to any significant degree. Hilary thought she looked exactly what she was: a hardworking, sober, businesswoman. At twenty-seven she was finally beginning to see signs of success and she was wearing the traditional little gray suit today to prove it. She wasn't particularly conscious of the fact that the blood-red blouse she had chosen to accompany the suit gave the outfit more than a touch of interest. It hinted at something more in its owner's character. Something of which the owner, herself, wasn't really aware.

"I'm terribly sorry, Miss . . .?" E. Morgan waited encouragingly for a name with which to finish the sentence but when it was not forthcoming, she went on hurriedly. "I'll let Mr. Saber know right away. He's been busy with a conference call, you understand. I'm sure he'll want you to go right in." The secretary punched the intercom button, speaking into the little mesh screen before her listener could even acknowledge the call.

"Mr. Saber, your . . . your fiancee is here. She's been waiting for quite some time . . ."

There was a distinct pause during which Hilary had to take a firm grip on her courage. She mustn't back down now. After all, this was nothing more than a business meeting. . . .

Finally, a marvelously gritty voice on the other end of the intercom said in a gentle rumble, "I'm sorry, Mrs. Morgan, I didn't quite catch the name . . ."

"I said your fiancee, Mr. Saber," E. Morgan repeated, looking a bit desperate as Hilary smiled benignly down at her.

"I see." Another pause. "Please send her in."

"This way, Miss . . ."

"Forrester," Hilary supplied, following obediently as E. Morgan rose from behind the desk and led the way toward an imposing door. "Hilary Forrester."

"Yes. I'm terribly sorry to have kept you waiting. I'm afraid that when you just said to tell Mr. Saber he had a visitor I rather assumed you were a salesperson. We get so many and they . . ."

"That's quite all right," Hilary assured her smoothly, wishing the butterflies in her stomach would find someplace to settle. It was difficult to calm E. Morgan and herself at the same time. The secretary opened the door.

"Miss Forrester, Sir," E. Morgan said politely, ushering Hilary into a richly plush office. A huge mahogany desk dominated the room. Hilary had very little chance to take in the details of the scene because a very tall, very broad-shouldered man was getting to his feet on the other side of the desk. In fact, Hilary thought vaguely, Logan Saber was probably best described as large. She was tall, herself, but she had to look up a goodly distance in order to meet his eyes. Yet for all his size there wasn't a hint of softness or extra weight anywhere on his well-muscled frame. In fact, the overall impression was that of a heavy, sleek jungle cat. And those cool, assessing, gray-green eyes didn't detract one bit from the image.

"Thank you Mrs. Morgan," Logan Saber said in that soft growl which seemed to emanate from somewhere deep in his chest. With a flick of the gray-green gaze he dismissed the interested secretary before turning to face his visitor.

Hilary felt herself growing warm beneath the impact of his narrowed gaze as it lazily raked her figure from the top of her tidy head to the toes of her well-shod feet. She opened her mouth, determined to get control of the interview from the beginning, but before she could say anything Logan Saber was already speaking.

"You will, I'm sure, forgive my small lapse, but I appear to have forgotten the, umm, precise details of our relationship, Miss Forrester," he said smoothly, coming around to the front of the huge desk and leaning against it, arms folded as he studied her.

Hilary drew a small breath, determined to be cool about the whole matter. "You can relax, Mr. Saber, I've come to save you from me. My name is Hilary and I'm Crawford Forrester's daughter." She waited briefly for the name to click into place although she knew from past experience that she wasn't at all what people generally expected. Any daughter of Crawford Forrester's ought to be beautiful, adventuresome and a bit reckless. Logan Saber, on the other hand, would undoubtedly turn out to be from the same mold as the others Crawford had chosen for her. He appeared to be a little older than the previous candidate, perhaps thirty-five or thirty-six and he wasn't nearly as handsome as the last one, but Saber had that successful look Crawford favored. In fact, Hilary decided suddenly, the man in front of her struck her as being the kind of person who would be thoroughly competent at whatever he involved himself with from women to business to sports. Definitely someone Crawford would want in the family.

Hilary noted the hard, rugged lines of Saber's face with its firm mouth and proud nose. No, not handsome, but strong. Too strong? Ridiculous, she assured herself quickly. She could handle the situation. The heavy pelt of his hair nearly matched the mahogany of his desk she found herself thinking suddenly and wondered why he kept it cut so short. Wasn't this one going to turn out to be as style conscious as the others had been? The gray suit he wore was a masculine version of her own. But unlike Hilary, this man probably had a whole closet full of such expensive clothes. And they would all fit him with the same hand-tailored look this one had.

"Crawford's daughter?" Logan Saber was saying thoughtfully. "I wasn't aware he had a daughter."

"You would have been made aware of the fact quite soon," Hilary assured him with a slightly rueful smile. "As soon as the deal for the restaurants got anywhere near closing." She took a seat with an air of nonchalance.

"I see. Please excuse my failure to keep up with the conversation. I seem to still be recovering from the shock of having my fiancee introduced to me by my secretary." Logan moved, an easy, coordinated motion which took him back behind the desk. He sat down and regarded his visitor with an effective, quelling sort of manner. "Let's start at the beginning, shall we? Suppose you explain exactly what it is you want to accomplish here, Miss Forrester."

"Of course," Hilary agreed briskly, forcing herself to be all business as she came to the embarrassing part of the discussion. "I'm sorry about telling your secretary I was your future wife, but I really have been kept waiting for some time and I have other things to do today. Mrs. Morgan thought I was a salesperson, you see . . ."

"Mrs. Morgan is well paid to ensure only necessary visitors make it into this room," Logan told her. "The indefinite wait is one of her favorite tactics. Normally it's very effective."

Hilary nodded, appreciating the situation. "I understand, but it's getting close to lunch and as I'm sure you'll have plans I wanted to get my business over with quickly. You see, Mr. Saber, the line I gave your secretary wasn't exactly a complete lie."

There was a weighty pause during which Logan Saber's only reaction was a rising eyebrow.

Hilary plunged in. "Were you aware that my father's restaurants have nearly been sold three times during the past year?"

"I knew there had been other negotiations, yes," the large man said coolly, the gray-green gaze watchful in a lazy, half-menacing way.

"Did Crawford tell you why the deals had failed to close?" Hilary persisted, wishing he wouldn't pin her with that particular look. This whole thing was hard enough as it was!

"We haven't discussed the issue. But I have the feeling you're about to enlighten me," he added drily.

"The deals fell through because the bargains were made contingent on the buyer marrying me," Hilary announced baldly, fighting down the wave of red she

10

knew was rising into her cheeks. This was so embarrassing!

"Really?" Logan Saber's inflection said it all: He didn't believe her.

Hilary sighed and tried again. "I know it's difficult to understand, especially since Crawford has yet to mention me to you, but it's true. I'm here today because I've run out of clever ideas for foiling my father's plans and I thought I'd try the straightforward approach; one businessperson to another."

Logan idly drummed the fingers of one large, square hand on the desk top while he studied her. The action reminded Hilary of the way a large cat might twitch the tip of its tail. There was a touch of impatience in the gesture and a small threat.

"You expect me to believe this story, Miss Forrester?" he finally asked in a low growl.

"No, not immediately," she admitted with an understanding smile. "I realize I'm not exactly what you would expect Crawford's daughter to look like. And if you were to get to know me you'd realize I don't behave as one would expect any daughter of his to behave. I don't even ski!"

"What's that got to do with the matter?" he asked in surprise.

"Skiing? Only that Crawford is very much a sportsman and I don't share his interests. That's part of the problem. You see, my father endowed me with his business sense but not his sense of adventure or his love of excitement. We get along very well, but he doesn't always understand me. And when it comes to my tastes in men, he's totally mystified. A year ago, shortly after my twenty-sixth birthday he decided he'd settle me down with the right kind of man. Crawford's afraid that I've become so totally devoted to my work that I'm not very bright where men are concerned. He's taken it

11

upon himself to insure I bring the right sort into the family and he's using the lure of his restaurants to do it."

"Your father and I have progressed quite a way in the discussions without your name having even been mentioned, Miss Forrester. Perhaps in my case he's made an exception?" Logan mocked.

"I doubt it. Tell me, has he invited you to his place in Santa Barbara yet?" As soon as she said it, Hilary knew she'd guessed right. She nodded, satisfied.

"How did you know about the invitation?" He hid his surprise well but it was too late.

"It's the usual routine," she said a little sadly. "At least I'm learning. The first two candidates and I were equally startled but by the time the third one had arrived on the scene I managed to figure out the pattern."

"And with me you think you've actually gotten a step ahead of your father, is that it?" Logan seemed amused, Hilary thought. He probably didn't believe a word she was saying.

"Exactly," she confirmed grimly.

"Tell me," he invited casually, "What's supposed to happen in Santa Barbara?"

"I live there," she explained patiently. "We'll be introduced when I'm asked to have dinner or something. By then you'll have been told what is expected of you."

"You think your father will tell me that if I'm really interested in getting the restaurants I'll offer to marry you?" he scoffed.

"Yes. That's the deal he made with the other three. Don't worry, the financial arrangements he'll offer will be terrific."

"The other three, er, candidates went for it?"

"I'd appreciate it if you wouldn't act so astonished,"

Hilary said wryly. "I mean, I realize I'm not the Playmate of the Year, but I do have a few redeeming characteristics. Which brings me to the bottom line. If and when I marry, it will be to someone capable of recognizing and appreciating those qualities. I will not be part of a business arrangement regardless of how right Crawford thinks the man is for me!" Her small chin lifted with unconscious firmness.

"You wish to marry for love?" he asked with a faint twitch of humor at the corner of his mouth.

"A silly eccentricity, I admit, but there you are. Say goodbye to the restaurants, Mr. Saber, or find a way to outmaneuver my father," Hilary said staunchly, letting some of her inner resolve show in her tone.

"Aren't you afraid you might be presenting me with a challenge?" he suggested softly.

She blinked, uncertain of his attitude.

"I'm attempting to reason with you, Mr. Saber," she replied carefully. "You should be grateful," she added with a sudden grin. "The other candidates weren't so lucky!"

"They, I gather, weren't treated to a friendly warning?"

"Not until they had already heard the deal my father was offering and had decided it was worth courting me. By then they had met me and decided I was going to be easy prey. After all, a woman like me should be damn grateful to have such men willing to marry her!"

"So how did you unconvince them?" Logan asked, sounding interested.

"You want a case by case account?" Hilary inquired archly.

"Yes," he said slowly, leaning forward to rest his arms on the desk while he watched her face intently. "I think I do. I'm beginning to find the whole thing quite fascinating!"

"Well," Hilary hesitated and then decided to let him have the facts. "Candidate number one took me by complete surprise. I was actually rather flattered to have such a good-looking, sophisticated man take such an interest in me. It didn't take long, however, to find out what was going on. My father was a little too obvious and number one wasn't as bright as he could have been. I won't go into details but suffice it to say I decided to opt out in a hurry. Since my erstwhile Romeo viewed the entire matter as a business deal I thought the easiest way to get rid of him was to throw myself at him like a lovesick Juliet. He had made it clear he didn't care for the clinging vine variety of female and when I started talking about babies and gardens, et cetera, he decided the restaurants weren't worth it."

"The man obviously lacked brains if he couldn't see that he was being tricked," Logan commented.

"Correct. The second candidate had a touch of insecurity in him so I took the approach of making him think I was willing to marry because Crawford wouldn't let me get my hands on the restaurants otherwise."

"You let number two know you intended to run the operation and were merely using him?"

"He fled almost immediately, much to Crawford's disgust. My father doesn't care for weak men, you see."

"I understand," Logan acknowledged politely. "Please continue."

"Candidate number three made it simple for me because I found out he had a severe craving for reckless blondes. I sicced my friend Julia on him and he succumbed immediately. Julia did me the favor of arranging to be seen with him at a local nightclub on a night he was supposed to be romancing me. My father considered the poor man hopelessly compromised and sent him packing."

"It sounds as if you were having a great deal of success with your various approaches," Logan noted coolly. "I suppose I should feel fortunate to get advance warning."

"I'm running out of clever ideas, Mr. Saber," Hilary returned calmly. "I have confronted my father with my feelings on the issue and he refuses to listen. Even claims I'm imagining his plots." She sighed. "I've decided not to be bothered playing any more stupid games."

"Games?" he queried consideringly. "I'm not so sure that what you've described could be construed as games. It sounds more like strategy. You seem to have analyzed the candidates' weaknesses and used those weaknesses against them." Logan sounded almost admiring, Hilary thought, struck by a strange, vague worry.

"At the time the methods I used appeared to be the easiest ways of achieving my goal. In your case, however, I have decided to give the straightforward approach a try. It will be so much easier on everyone concerned if it works."

"What? You mean I don't get an opportunity to deal with a clinging female or prove my ability to handle the restaurants and keep a wife in line?"

"Or meet Julia," Hilary concluded with a smile.

"Oh, yes, the reckless blonde. Now that will be a pity, but then, reckless blondes are fairly common these days. You, on the other hand, strike me as not being out of an easily described mold. It's no wonder your father is having problems matching you up with the right man," Logan said smoothly, gray-green eyes gleaming with laughter.

"It's not for lack of trying," Hilary retorted ruefully. "The problem, of course, is that he's trying to match me up with *his* sort of man."

"And you want nothing to do with the type?"

"Nothing at all," she declared firmly, feeling a bit more relaxed now as Logan Saber appeared to be taking her news in stride.

"What sort of man, exactly, are we discussing? You say someone your father likes . . ." Logan asked with mild interest, settling back into the huge chair, his eyes never leaving her face.

"Your sort, I imagine," she smiled. "Crawford always chooses the ones who have the same interests as himself. He makes certain they're successful business types, too."

"What are your father's interests, Hilary? The ones he wants your husband to have?"

"Mr. Saber, I don't see any point in having our discussion go off on this particular tangent. You've met my father, you must be aware of what constitutes his sort of man," Hilary began determinedly.

"Come now, after exploding your little grenade and telling me I have no chance at acquiring the restaurants, the least you can do is humor me with some casual conversation," Logan smiled. Hilary wasn't sure she liked the smile. It had a waiting quality to it that was slightly unnerving. Still, he did have a point. If he was going to prove reasonable she was willing to be polite.

"My father is a very dynamic man, Mr. Saber," she began slowly. "He's in his early sixties but he still skis, drives expensive, racy cars, maintains a string of women friends and generally lives a playboy existence. He's also a good businessman. He owns a yacht and flies his own plane. He's a classic male chauvinist who thinks a woman needs a strong man in order to be happy. I think that about sums it up. Do you see yourself in my little portrait? With a slight adjustment for your age, naturally?"

"It's obvious you see me that way," he mused.

Hilary shrugged, not very interested in the semantics of the situation. It was clear to her that Crawford would never have begun the restaurant negotiations with Logan Saber if her father hadn't seen the younger man as the right mate for his daughter.

"Well, Mr. Saber . . ." she began, getting easily to her feet.

"Please call me Logan," he corrected, also rising. "After all, we came so close to getting married that it seems ridiculous to be addressing each other by our last names, don't you think?"

"All right, Logan," she smiled, holding out a hand in polite farewell. "I hope you'll remember what I've said today when you consider the invitation my father has extended. I realize he can be very persuasive, but along with his business abilities, I've also inherited his stubbornness. I love my father, but I will not allow him to manage my life."

"I'll keep our discussion in mind." Logan paused holding her hand a moment longer than necessary. "And having promised to do so, may I suggest we celebrate our little understanding with lunch? I'm hungry and there's a pleasant little place around the corner. Unless you have other plans?"

Hilary frowned, taken by surprise. "I really don't think . . ."

"Please, Hilary?" he asked. "As a reward for my reasonableness?" There was a spark of humor in his eyes which reached her own sense of amusement.

"Your reasonableness? Does that mean I'm going to be spared the pains of concocting clever schemes to avoid marrying you?" she laughed.

17

"Are you kidding? I know a ruthless business type when I see one. It just so happens that I find myself free today and would prefer not to eat alone."

"Thank you very much," Hilary began again as she turned to go, "But I have a lot to do before catching my plane back to Santa Barbara. I'm sure you'll find someone . . ." she broke off the airy conclusion of her refusal as she caught sight of the glass case in the corner of the room. She hadn't noticed it when entering and now she hurried forward with delight.

"Salt cellars!" she exclaimed, charmed immediately as she stood looking down into the case with its array of delicate little bowls and spoons. "Do you collect them?" she asked, glancing up at Logan who had moved to stand behind her.

"Yes," he admitted readily, watching her reaction as she turned back to study the contents of the case. "Do you?"

"Oh, yes. I love them. In fact . . ." Hilary undid the clasp of her purse and rummaged around inside until she withdrew a small package. "I picked this up at a little antique store near this building before I came to see you. Isn't it gorgeous?" With loving hands, Hilary unwrapped the tissue from the small salt bowl, holding it out for his inspection.

With a last glance at her enthusiastic expression, Logan took the tiny little salt into his huge hand, grasping it with due care.

"A very nice piece of Meissen," he said after examining the small object with a knowing eye. "It has the old crossed-swords mark."

"I know. I'm delighted to find it," Hilary chuckled, taking the salt cellar back and beginning to rewrap it. "I must see what you've got," she rushed on, storing the package in her purse and leaning forward to examine Logan Saber's collection.

18

"I'm rather proud of that little Tiffany salt," Logan remarked, opening the lid of the case so she could get a closer view.

"It's beautiful," Hilary breathed admiringly, picking up the iridescent bowl and turning it upside down. "Signed, too. What a lucky find. Where did you get it?"

"At a shop in Beverly Hills. I'll be glad to show you . . ." he began deliberately.

"Oh, that's all right. I've spent as much as I should today and if I saw anything this lovely, I'd probably give in to temptation," Hilary assured him, hastily replacing the salt cellar. "You've got a good collection of the spoons, too," she went on brightly, picking up one or two of the tiny things and admiring them. "They're getting so hard to discover!"

"I know. How large is your collection?" he asked, holding the lid as Hilary dipped again and again into the case to examine the bowls.

"I have about fifty," she told him, conscious of his large frame standing so close. But the lure of the salt cellars was overpowering and against her better judgment, she continued to investigate. "You must have almost a hundred in here," she added.

"It's gotten to the point where I'll have to get another case if I'm going to keep adding to the collection," he replied ruefully. "I keep telling myself I'm going to stop, but as soon as I give myself the advice, I find another interesting item."

"I understand exactly how you feel," she grinned, reaching greedily for an unusual silver salt on a small pedestal. "I prefer to think of it as a vice and everyone is allowed a few vices."

"That's an idea," he smiled. "I could think of all the money I've saved over the years by not smoking and justify it that way."

Hilary turned laughing eyes up to him, withdrawing

19

reluctantly from the treasure chest. There was an unexpected pause as she found him studying her with his intent look and before she could gather her wits to make her escape, Logan was speaking quietly.

"Surely anyone who collects salt cellars and who has shown himself so reasonable in matters of business can't be much of a threat," he said gently. "Won't you let me take you out for a bite? It's the least I can do to thank you for the warning."

"Which you're going to heed?" she shot back quickly, knowing she should end the visit immediately but unable to ignore the genuineness of his invitation.

"You may rest assured I absorbed every word," he retorted laconically. "And since you're denying me the restaurants, it seems only appropriate that you should pay for my lunch, now that I think about it!"

Hilary laughed, relieved. "I thought you were going to take me out in gratitude for the warning!"

"I've changed my mind," he retorted smoothly.

It was, Hilary had cause to realize later, the best approach he could possibly have used. The combination of finding out that he collected salt cellars and that he wasn't in the least upset about the idea of letting her pay for lunch was her undoing.

"All right," she said, coming to a decision. "I'll buy you lunch. You have, indeed, turned out to be quite rational about the whole thing. To tell you the truth, I was a little nervous about coming here," she went on honestly as he opened the office door quickly, apparently afraid she might change her mind.

"You amaze me," he grinned, glancing down at her as she went past him. "You certainly seemed all business when you walked through this door. Very cool and very determined."

"Well, I was determined, but I wasn't really very

cool. You have to admit it was an awkward situation . . ." she broke off as E. Morgan glanced up expectantly.

"Ah, Mrs. Morgan," Logan said lightly, taking Hilary's arm and guiding her through the outer office. "I'll be back in a while. My future wife is hungry and she's going to take me out to lunch."

Hilary stiffened at once but when she flicked a frowning glance upward it was to meet a blandly humorous one. Logan was only trying to make light of the situation, she realized, relaxing again.

"Of course, Mr. Saber," E. Morgan replied with the pleasant tones of the well-trained secretary. "Have a good time."

"Thank you," Logan smiled back. "It's bound to be an interesting meal." He swept Hilary through the outer door and down the hall to the elevators. "Sorry about that," he apologized at once. "Somehow it just seemed easier not to go into long explanations. There will be questions enough later," he added wryly.

"I realize that," Hilary smiled apologetically. "I shouldn't have used that particular line to get in to see you. Mrs. Morgan will be waiting for an invitation to the wedding!"

"I'm glad you have some sense of responsibility about what you've done," he teased, stepping into the elevator behind her and punching the lobby button. "I don't suppose you're willing to furnish me with an appropriate story I can use to explain your sudden appearance and disappearance in my life?"

"How about something along the lines of how we weren't suited to each other? She's bound to buy that. I know I must be a world apart from your usual type of woman!" Hilary suggested easily.

"That much is true," he acknowledged with a

readiness that hurt for some reason. "I'll think about it. Perhaps something even more clever will occur to us at lunch."

"Do you own many restaurants, Mr. Saber . . . I mean, Logan?" Hilary said in an effort to make pleasant conversation as they walked out of the highrise office building and onto the busy Los Angeles sidewalk.

"A few," he admitted. "My company has a variety of interests. Restaurants such as your father's, which have shown themselves profitable and which fit into our chain are always welcome additions. We steer clear of exotic gourmet businesses because we aren't set up to manage such places. Our goal is to obtain pleasant, profitable, middle-American style restaurants. What about you? What's the line of work which has so captivated you your father is afraid he's going to have to do your husband hunting?" Logan gripped her arm firmly as they walked. It was rather like being hauled along by an irresistible force, Hilary thought with an inner smile.

"I've followed in my father's footsteps," she said lightly. "Except that my restaurant is nothing like his type of business. I've made it a point to create an unusual menu and have a good selection of wine. I wouldn't let a frozen entree through my receiving doors and that's the exact opposite of how my father runs his places! He's made a fortune on controlled-portion frozen entrees. My customers can rest assured that the food they eat is very fresh and even good for them which is becoming important to more and more people."

"You're running a health food restaurant?" he asked, guiding her through the door of a small, intimate cafe on the corner.

"I don't think of it in those terms. I have a degree in business but I've also got a lifelong interest in gourmet cooking. I've tried to combine the two," she explained, letting her words trail off as someone came forward to seat them. It was clear by the deferential treatment he received that Logan was a valued customer.

"You must eat here frequently," Hilary observed as people scurried forward to attend them.

"If you're referring to the quality of the service," he retorted ruefully, "I'm afraid I have to confess I owe it to overtipping."

"Better not tell anyone I'm paying for today's meal, then, until it's time to leave!"

"I don't intend to make a secret out of the fact that you're taking me to lunch," he smiled, picking up the menu. "This is the first time in my life that a woman's treated me. I plan to enjoy the novelty!"

"Really?" Hilary said, surprised. "I was under the impression times have changed."

"I take it you do this frequently?" he inquired dryly, eyeing her enigmatically.

"I've picked up my share of checks, yes," she said calmly, thinking of how many times she had fed Kevin Thorne. "Why shouldn't I? I can afford it."

"And doing so helps insure that the relationship stays on an equal basis?" he concluded perceptively.

"There's nothing like maintaining sound financial arrangements to keep 'relationships' as you call them on an equal footing," she agreed smoothly.

"Your father has trained you well," he said quietly.

"Too well, according to him," Hilary smiled. "He's afraid he's created a woman who won't be able to find herself the right kind of man. That's why he's taken on the task, himself."

"But you have other plans?" Logan asked, closing the padded menu firmly.

"Definitely." Hilary made the word very final. She had no intention of discussing her future romantic prospects with this man! "You know," she went on, deliberately changing the subject. "Your salt cellar collection surprised me."

"How's that?"

"Well, the kind of male Crawford usually favors would collect something along the lines of antique swords or duelling pistols, if he collected anything at all."

"Your father doesn't know about my salt cellar collection. Perhaps if he did, he would remove me from the list of candidates," Logan said.

"Perhaps. It really doesn't matter much now, though, does it? You and I understand each other, I think. You will either find another way to buy the restaurants from my father or you'll give up the project altogether."

There was a pause before Logan said in his soft growl, "Yes, Hilary Forrester, I think I'm beginning to understand you. But I'm not too sure you understand me."

When Hilary glanced up quickly, eyes narrowed, it was to find Logan blandly eating his salad.

Chapter Two

Several hours after her lunch with Logan Saber, the small commuter plane Hilary had taken from Los Angeles landed in Santa Barbara. It was with her usual feeling of relief that she deplaned at the small airport, found her luggage easily and walked briskly out to the nearby parking lot. Such a change from L.A. International, she thought for the hundredth time, grateful not to have to wrestle the traffic, the miles of corridors and the confusing parking lots. Why anyone would actually want to live in Los Angeles was beyond her. She took a deep breath of the clear air, thought of the smog she had left behind and smiled. Here in the sunny little community by the sea she had made a home for herself and she knew she had chosen well.

With a casual gesture Hilary slung her small bag into the backseat of her sensible little car and started the engine. The restaurant was closed today, a Monday, and she momentarily thought about stopping by just to check on things and then laughed at herself for being so anxious. Her small staff was extremely competent and she knew she could probably disappear for quite some time without having any bad news awaiting her when she returned. She would never do such a thing, of course. She loved the Silver Salt Cellar and couldn't imagine deliberately walking away from it.

She avoided the temptation to look in on the restaurant and drove straight to her small condominium on the hillside overlooking the town and the sea. There was plenty of daylight left and the thought of pouring herself a glass of wine and relaxing on the veranda while she watched the sun go down held a lot of appeal. Besides, she admitted ruefully to herself as she pulled into the drive and hoisted her bag out of the backseat, she had a lot to think about this afternoon.

The interview with Logan Saber had gone tolerably well, she reflected with a certain satisfaction as she changed into a pair of jeans, poured the promised glass of wine and made her way through the cheerful living room with its expanse of windows to the veranda. There she settled back in a lounger and considered the day. Yes, Logan had seemed reasonable enough after he'd begun to realize she was telling him the truth. After the technique she had used to gain access to his office, it was a wonder he'd been so tolerant!

The lie hadn't really been necessary, Hilary thought honestly. She could just as easily have said she was Crawford Forrester's daughter and probably gotten the same response. But the small shock value imparted by the fabrication had, for some reason, been irresistible at the time. That wasn't like her, Hilary admonished herself. But sometimes these little mischievous urges came over one. . . . She found herself grinning.

"Take that, Crawford," she said aloud, lifting her glass with a flourish. "Maybe one of these days you'll realize I really am your daughter in more ways than one!"

Yes, she congratulated herself warmly, she had effectively nipped her father's plans in the bud this time. Logan Saber wouldn't get involved in any deal that involved her now that he realized she knew the truth. Frankly, Hilary told herself, she wasn't at all certain he would have gone along with Crawford's plans anyway. Logan hadn't seemed quite as greedy as the others. Perhaps the restaurants didn't seem so important to him as they had to the first three candidates. Well, she would never see the big man again so there was little point in rehashing the events of the day endlessly. Still, she had rather enjoyed the lunch, even if she had paid for it! Once they had arrived at an understanding they had at least been able to make decent conversation.

But between herself and a man like Logan Saber there could never be anything more, she thought firmly, helping herself to a handful of pretzels. He may have been a more interesting conversationalist than the other candidates, but he was still very much the kind of man she avoided like the plague. Actually, she thought wryly, sipping the wine consideringly, avoiding such men wasn't so very difficult. The truth of the matter was that they tended to have very little interest in a woman like herself. Except, naturally, when Crawford was trying to maneuver them into marriage with his daughter!

The week passed swiftly with business at the restaurant proceeding along the smooth, orderly lines Hilary insisted upon. As usual, she spent a great deal of time working on the accounts, supervising deliveries and dealing with the staff. The Silver Salt Cellar catered to the downtown business and tourist crowd during the lunch hours and, after a successful experiment, offered a genuine afternoon tea which had proved enormously popular. Dinner was only served on Friday and Saturday nights but Hilary was seriously considering staying open all week for the evening meal. The recent addition of a Sunday brunch had been her latest effort and, like the afternoon tea, had obtained almost instant success.

It was toward the end of the Sunday brunch rush that week when one of the waitresses, an attractive young girl who went to school at the nearby university, poked her head into the kitchen.

"Someone out front to see you, Hilary," the girl called and ducked back out with a loaded tray.

Hilary glanced up from the hollandaise sauce she was supervising and frowned.

"Go ahead, Hilary," the serious young man who was the chef said quickly. "I've got the crepes under control. I'll take over the sauce."

"Thanks, Ben," she smiled, untying the apron which was protecting a casual skirt and blouse. "I'll be back as soon as I can." She headed toward the swinging door. "Probably some customer had gotten a bad bottle of champagne!"

She walked from the bustle of the kitchen into the dining room which, with its neat black and white tiles, hanging plants and quiet booths seemed a world apart. Hilary made a point of seeing that her customers could relax over their meals.

"Who wanted to see me, Sheila?" she asked quietly, scanning the crowd as she came up behind the waitress.

"The gentleman over there at the table for two by the window, Hilary. He said he . . ."

"My father!" Hilary exclaimed, spotting Crawford's fine profile almost immediately. "So he decided to spend some time here after all," she went on musingly, half under her breath. "I thought when I squelched his latest plan he . . ." Then she realized there was someone else in the booth. She couldn't see the other person, but the table was clearly set for two.

"Don't tell me he found another candidate so soon," she muttered angrily. Her amber eyes narrowed in sudden premonition as she started forward with a determined step.

"Another what?" Sheila asked curiously but Hilary was already halfway across the room, skirting the huge wine rack which stood in the center.

It was as she rounded the rack that she finally saw the other occupant of the small booth and it was all she could do to keep from groaning aloud.

Logan Saber, she thought bitterly. He never intended to abide by the little "understanding." The man was just as greedy as all the others. Perhaps the fact that she had consented to have lunch with him the day of the confrontation had led him to believe she could be easily charmed. Well, Logan Saber could think again, Hilary told herself furiously, sweeping to a halt by the offending table.

"Good morning, Crawford," she said with patently false sweetness, conscious of the people in nearby booths. She ignored Logan completely but that didn't stop her from being painfully aware of the intent regard of those gray-green eyes. She experienced an almost uncontrollable desire to pick up the vase of fresh flowers and fling it at him. Which act, when she considered it, was such an incredibly violent reaction for her that she was somewhat shocked.

"Did you decide to spend some time at the cottage this week?" she continued to her father.

Trim and attractive with a heavy mane of silver hair and the amber eyes he had passed on to his daughter, Crawford Forrester grinned cheerfully, getting to his feet to plant an affectionate kiss on Hilary's cheek.

"I heard the weather was scheduled to be fantastic here this weekend and L.A. is full of smog, as usual," Crawford shrugged. "So I phoned my friend Logan and suggested we spend some time in sunny Santa Barbara. I've been wanting to take the boat out again." Crawford paused, turning to a silent Logan who had risen to his feet behind his host. Hilary realized with a small pang that he was even bigger than she had remembered.

"Let me introduce Logan Saber, Hilary. A business associate. Logan, my daughter, Hilary."

"We've met," Hilary said coldly, paying no attention whatsoever to Logan's outstretched hand. "Didn't Mr. Saber tell you?" She flicked a mocking glance up at the tall man and then quickly returned her gaze to her father. "It won't work, Crawford. Just as it hasn't worked for the last three times," she hissed. "Your 'business associate' knows that. I've already told him! Enjoy your stay in Santa Barbara and if you're planning on any entertaining, count me out!"

She barely had time to see Crawford's brows lift in astonishment before she whirled on her heel and prepared to stride off to the kitchen, her neatly braided head held high. But before she could take a step a large, strong hand whipped out to snag her wrist, completely enclosing her fingers.

"One moment, Hilary," Logan's dark, velvet voice ordered softly as he spoke for the first time. "Your father and I . . ." he broke off for a split second, watching the flags of battle in her cheeks just as if he knew she was only waiting until he finished his comment before she sailed into him again.

"Your father and I," he continued deliberately, not releasing her hand, "would like to see the wine list, if you don't mind."

Hilary blinked in surprise, taken off balance for an

instant. She had been expecting a denial or a justification for his presence and he knew it! She recovered quickly, glancing pointedly at her still-trapped hand.

"I'll be happy to have it sent to your table, Mr. Saber," she said coolly.

"Excellent," he approved, eyes gleaming wickedly. "We'll be wanting something light, I think, to go with the cheese crepes."

"I'm sure you'll find something appropriate on our list. Will there be anything else, Mr. Saber?" she asked with a sort of grim patience. She tried tugging unobtrusively at her hand but it felt as if it were enclosed in steel. On the other side of the table she could see her father watching the little byplay with a deeply interested expression.

"There is one other small thing," Logan drawled deliberately, letting her feel the strength of his fingers. He knew, Hilary realized, that she would go to any lengths not to draw the customer's attention.

"Yes?" she prompted coldly.

"An apology, I think," he suggested quietly, sitting down again and not releasing her hand. Crawford also resumed his seat, his eyes on his daughter.

"An apology!" she echoed a low, furious tone. "I don't owe you an apology for anything, Mr. Saber!"

"Not me," he corrected mildly. "Your father."

For a moment Hilary stared at him and then she turned abruptly to Crawford, lifting her manacled hand to clearly display Logan's grip.

"Well, Crawford," she began wryly, "You managed to pick a truly masterful type this time, didn't you?" She dropped her wrist again, Logan's fingers still wrapped around it. "Aren't you afraid he'll be the kind who beats his women?"

"I didn't raise a fool of a daughter," Crawford returned easily, trying to hide a grin and failing

31

miserably. "I'm sure you'll have more sense than to push Logan that far."

Her eyes amber crystals, Hilary swung her gaze back to Logan who appeared to be willing to sit there all morning awaiting the apology.

"Well?" he prompted unhurriedly. "Why don't you get it over with, Hilary and then I'll let you go back to your precious kitchen."

"Why should I apologize?" she challenged angrily. It was getting increasingly difficult to keep her voice down.

"Because you've accused your father of plotting when you have absolutely no evidence," he informed her mildly, but the expression in his eyes was far from mild.

"No evidence?" she repeated slowly, striving to bring her temper under control. Hilary couldn't even remember the last time she had been so close to losing it. It was an unnerving feeling. "Your presence here is all the evidence I need, Mr. Saber!"

"It doesn't occur to you that I might have wanted to come to Santa Barbara for other than business reasons?" he inquired politely.

"No," she said shortly. "Not when you show up with Crawford. And not when Crawford has a history of . . ." Hilary broke off as, out of the corner of her eye, she caught sight of a familiar figure entering the restaurant. In a moment the man would glance her way, see her talking to Logan and Crawford and wonder if she needed assistance. The thought of a fracas in front of customers . . .

Without a moment's hesitation, Hilary turned to her father. "Crawford, if I've misjudged this little scene, you have my sincerest apologies. I'm sorry I got upset over such a trivial event, anyhow. It doesn't really matter in the long run if you are plotting, does it? I've already proven I can hold my own when it comes to those kind of games. Sorry I lost my temper. I'll keep things in perspective from here on. Forgive me?" she added sweetly.

Crawford looked understandably astonished at her sudden capitulation. He gazed for a second at Hilary and then turned a smiling look on Logan.

"My congratulations, Logan, I never would have thought . . . oh. I see now why Hilary was so anxious to apologize all of a sudden." He was staring across the room, a thoughtfully disapproving expression on his face.

Before any further comment could be made, Hilary wriggled her trapped hand. "I believe you promised to release me as soon as the apology was made, Mr. Saber?"

"So I did," he grinned unlocking her wrist, his eyes following Crawford's gaze. The grin faded as he saw the good-looking, sandy-haired young man dressed in a blue workshirt and jeans.

Hilary didn't hang around to explain. Crawford would do that, she thought ruefully. He didn't particularly care for Kevin Thorne. She walked through the room to where Kevin stood waiting, smiling at customers as she went. Some of these people were becoming regulars and she wanted to keep them faithful.

"Good morning, Kevin," she said brightly as she drew close. "Come for breakfast?"

"Wouldn't miss it. You know it must be good if I'm willing to sacrifice the morning light for it!" He bent his shaggy head, giving her a brief, casual kiss of greeting. "Got a table?"

"I'm sure we can find one," she replied. "The rush has pretty well passed. We'll have you fed and back to your painting in no time!"

"Some things are worth lingering over," he grinned

33

cheerfully, following her to a small table on the other side of the room from Crawford and Logan.

"Have a seat," she told him. "I'll send Sheila over with the coffee."

"Sounds great. Was that your father I saw you talking with as I came in?"

"Yes, he's in town for a while. Plans to do some sailing," Hilary said briefly.

"And the man with him?" Kevin pressed interestedly, eyeing Hilary with a knowing look.

"Another one," she admitted. Kevin knew all about Crawford's matchmaking.

"I thought so. Your father is pretty persistent, isn't he? I keep telling you, love, there's one sure-fire way to put a halt to his matchmaking . . ." Kevin let the sentence trail off suggestively.

Hilary smiled down at him as he took his seat. "One of these days I'm going to take you up on your offer of marriage and then what will you do?"

"Eat free at the Silver Salt Cellar for the rest of my life," he chuckled, drawing an answering laugh from Hilary.

"Just another free-loading artist," she scolded. "I'd better get back to the kitchen. See you later, Kevin."

"You bet. In fact, why don't you drop around tonight? I'll pick up a bottle of wine and some cheese and we can watch the sunset. We'll both be watching it separately anyway. Might as well do it together."

"Sold. After such a romantic invitation, how could I refuse," Hilary grinned and turned to start back toward the kitchen. Unexpectedly her eyes encountered Logan Saber's as she moved toward the swinging doors. He had been watching her with Kevin. She knew those gray-green eyes hadn't missed a thing and she told herself she was glad. It would show him that she wasn't Crawford's lonely daughter who would be easily swept

34

off her feet by any man willing to take the time to apply himself to the task!

But even as she escaped into the kitchen, Hilary acknowledged there had been a disturbingly intent quality in Saber's expression as he'd met her eyes. It was a look she hadn't seen before in any of Crawford's other candidates and it sent a small shiver of warning down her erect little spine. Candidate number four, she knew intuitively, meant business. If he had decided to marry Hilary in order to gain the restaurants, she was going to have her hands full defeating him. Something told her that Logan Saber was going to be a much more difficult opponent than the other three . . .

"But," she found herself telling Kevin Thorne that evening as they sipped wine on the patio of his cottage near the sea. "There's always the chance that he really is here with Crawford on an honest vacation. I suppose I shouldn't worry about it until he makes a clearly incriminating move!"

"If he's anything like the others, he won't wait long before he tries his hand at courting you," Kevin replied, slicing another wedge of cheese and handing it to her on a cracker.

"Well this time, I'm not going to fool around. I'll just tell him straight out that I won't even go out with him, much less . . ."

"You tried that with candidates number two and three as I recall," Kevin reminded her pointedly. "They just kept pestering you until you finally resorted to your little schemes."

"I know. There's something about wealthy, successful businessmen that makes them believe they can have almost any woman they want. Especially a woman like me!" Hilary sighed. "Now, if I were more like Julia . . . more dashing and beautiful, I could probably intimidate them . . ."

"Well, you're not like Julia," Kevin told her firmly. "You're a nice, sensible, level-headed businesswoman and you can use those tactics just as successfully as Julia wields her, er, charms."

"Thank you for those comforting words," Hilary retorted ruefully.

Kevin laughed. "Sorry, love, but it's the truth and we both know it."

"You're absolutely right, of course, but don't you think you should occasionally practice the skills of flattery? I mean, every artist has to compromise once in a while and give the client what he or she wants, rather than the unvarnished truth," Hilary mocked.

"That's true. Maybe that's why I've been so incredibly unsuccessful at getting you into my bed," Kevin grinned unabashedly.

"You've been unsuccessful because deep down we both recognize the fact that we were born to be friends with each other; not lovers."

"That's not what your father thinks," he reminded her, biting down on his cheese and cracker. "Crawford's deathly afraid we're having an affair, you know. I realized that on the one occasion when you introduced us. That was about a year ago, wasn't it?" he continued thoughtfully. "Maybe that's why the candidates started appearing, Hilary."

"Because Crawford thinks I'm in danger of marrying an artist instead of a businessman?"

"Or worse, moving in with an artist instead of a businessman," Kevin chuckled.

Hilary considered the information. Crawford had never said much about Kevin Thorne; he hadn't needed to say anything. It was clear he didn't approve of the young artist, but Hilary put that down to the fact that Crawford would never approve of a male who didn't fit his image of success.

"That might have been what set him off on his campaign to find a husband for me," she mused, "But whatever the reason, I'm getting fed up with the effort. For both their sakes, Logan and Crawford had better be telling me the truth when they claim there's no business deal involving me in the works!"

"Or else?"

"Or else," she confirmed with a determined nod of her head.

"You remind me of your father when you look like that," Kevin teased.

"Just remember that it's only people like my father and I, business types, who will be able to afford your art in a few years. Better be nice to us," Hilary countered, grinning.

"Keep reminding me," he told her, pouring out the last of the wine. "Want to go to a film this evening?" he added casually.

"If there's one playing that's got a happy ending," she agreed.

"You know I need the sad ending kind," he complained. "How else can I get myself into a properly depressed, tortured, artistic mood."

"The last time I let you drag me to one of those awful, dismal foreign things I had nightmares for a week. It's one with a happy ending or it's no dice," Hilary said firmly.

"Oh, well. Maybe we can find a rerun of Bambi somewhere," Kevin groaned.

They compromised and went to a new musical which had just come to town and which Hilary enjoyed thoroughly.

"So romantic," she exclaimed afterward as she drove Kevin back to his cottage. They had flipped a coin to see who would do the driving and she'd lost.

"So unrealistic," he groused cheerfully. "You know,

sometimes you still surprise me, Hilary love. One would think you'd prefer something more substantial and more true-to-life than that drivel!"

"Who knows," she chided lightly, "Maybe I've got a secret layer of undiscovered passion lying dormant deep within my mercenary little business soul."

"Care to come inside and experiment?" Kevin invited wickedly.

Hilary looked disappointed and regretful. "Gee, Kevin, I'd really love to give it a whirl, but you know how it is. I'm an early riser and I really should be getting home to my own bed. Tomorrow I'll have to spend a lot of time on my books for the restaurant and I like to be fresh when I tackle my finances!"

"Excuses, excuses," he said, climbing out of the car and closing the door. "Take care of yourself, love," he went on, leaning down to speak to her through the open window. "I'll give you a call in a couple of days. I'm working on something I'd like you to see. It's for a local bank that's opening a new office and wants a landscape for one of the walls."

"Commercial art, Kevin?" Hilary queried mockingly.

"Art that pays," he corrected smoothly. "Anyhow, I'd like your opinion."

"A sort of businessperson's point of view?"

"Exactly."

"How flattering," she teased. "Don't worry," she added quickly. "I'll be glad to critique it."

She drove back up the hill that led to her condominium complex with the kind of absent awareness one uses when driving a familiar route. But even if she had been more alert, Hilary probably wouldn't have paid much attention to the strange car parked near her driveway. She would have assumed it belonged to friends of one

38

of the neighbors. As it was, she barely even glanced at it. She had a lot to think about.

Perhaps she had overreacted this morning when she'd first seen her father with Logan Saber, she told herself, switching off the engine and climbing out of the vehicle. If Crawford had taken a personal liking to Logan it was conceivable that, even if the restaurant deal wasn't going to work, he still might invite Logan to spend some time at his Santa Barbara retreat. But that didn't wash, either. Crawford's friends tended to be much closer to his own age. Except for the women friends, of course, Hilary thought wryly, walking up the steps to her front door and fishing around inside her bag for the key.

Well, she thought as she turned the key in the lock, there was still another alternative. Perhaps Crawford really had decided to sell the restaurants, regardless of whether or not the buyer was willing to marry into the family as part of the deal. Her father certainly didn't need the profits. His business investments over the years were more than sufficient to allow him to continue to maintain his choice of lifestyle. But he had seemed so adamant about using the restaurants to snag a proper mate for his daughter that she couldn't get rid of the instinctive feeling he was still trying.

Her hand was groping for the hall light when a voice spoke from the dark depths of a living room chair.

"Hello, Hilary," A deep, gritty, velvety voice that Hilary would have recognized anywhere.

"Logan!" she said in a muted screech, startled nearly out of her wits. "What on earth are you doing in my home?" she went on, saying the first thing which came to mind. The adrenaline induced by the surprise was pumping madly through her bloodstream and she had to take a couple of deep breaths to calm herself. She finished the task of flipping the lightswitch which succeeded in throwing Logan Saber's large frame into shadowy relief.

He was reclining in a chair near the window, apparently enjoying the view of the town at night.

"I came to see you," he informed her in a deceptively simple tone, turning his head to glance at her. Even in the poor light she could see the coolly assessing glitter in those gray-green eyes. "You weren't home," he continued, lifting a hand apologetically, "so I let myself in and settled down to enjoy your view while I waited for you."

"Of all the nerve," she began heatedly, moving forward to snap on a lamp. "Of all the arrogant, nerve! You can just remove yourself immediately!" She came to a stop in front of him, hands on her hips, amber eyes glaring.

Logan's gaze ran over her from her sandals to her jeans and on up to the cream-colored shirt. "That's a nice scarf," he said softly, his eyes settling on the brilliantly patterned scrap of silk, the only touch of color in her attire.

"Get out of here," she snapped, ignoring his lazy appraisal.

"I haven't answered your question yet," he retorted easily.

"What question?" she blazed.

"The one about what I'm doing in your home," he reminded her.

"I'm sure you haven't got a good answer, so there's no point in pursuing it," she told him. "I want you out of here!"

"Not yet. We need to talk, you and I," he said quietly. "Why don't you have a seat," he added politely, as if it were his home.

"I prefer to stand."

"Suit yourself," he sighed. "But good manners demand I do the same if you insist on staying on your feet." He got slowly out of the chair until he was standing in front of her, towering over her smaller frame. The point was clear. Standing over her like this he was all the more intimidating.

Say what you want to say," Hilary groaned, flopping angrily into the nearest seat, "and then remove yourself. Did my father send you?"

"You insist on blaming your father for my presence anywhere near you, Hilary," he said, frowning. In the lamplight his mahogany-brown hair gleamed richly and the hard planes of his face seemed to have been carved with a blade. He was dressed in a casual, open-necked shirt and slacks which looked expensive, if a bit conservative.

"Sorry," Hilary retorted flippantly. "Habit, I suppose. I'd forgotten you wanted to pretend this was all your idea."

"Being here tonight is most definitely my idea," he said coolly.

"Why?" she asked bluntly, watching him with narrowed eyes.

"I had to know how fierce the competition was," he informed her with a shrug.

Hilary looked blank for a moment and then his meaning became clear. "The competition for my favors?" she clarified, finding it an effort to keep her temper under control.

"What else?"

"You might be more concerned about the competition for the restaurants!"

"In your mind it's one and the same, isn't it?"

"True," she admitted, wanting to hit him. This was ridiculous! She must get herself under control. With a deliberate effort of will, she smiled with a frosty curve of her lip. "How important are the restaurants to you, Logan? Important enough to fight another man for me?"

"I would, naturally, prefer a less violent solution to the problem of dealing with competition," he said smoothly.

"How sad," she pouted mockingly. "And here I was hoping I'd finally found myself in the romantic position of having two men ready to do battle over me! Julia would have been so envious!"

"Julia?" he frowned briefly and then relaxed. "Oh, yes. The dashing blonde. The one you used on candidate number two, if I recall correctly."

"Candidate number three," she said kindly. "Candidate number two was the insecure one."

"The one you terrified with your super, high-powered career woman approach," he nodded. "Whichever one it was, let's return to the business at hand."

He fixed Hilary with the sort of look she imagined lions gave potential victims. "Tell me about your friend, the artist."

"From the fact that you know his line of work, I have a feeling my father has already given you plenty of details," she ground out scathingly. "I don't intend to discuss Kevin with you!"

"A close friend?"

"Very close!"

"But not so close that you choose to spend the night with him, apparently."

"Not this particular night," Hilary inserted with a lift of her firm chin. An idea was beginning to take shape in her mind. If Logan Saber thought she was involved in an affair with Kevin he might decide the competition was more than he wished to tackle.

"You have a rather casual arrangement?" he suggested softly, but Hilary didn't care for the look which flashed for an instant in those gray-green eyes.

Without answering Hilary merely inclined her head in a regal fashion, letting him believe what he wished.

"I see," he said almost gently. "Your father was afraid that might be the case. His biggest worry is that you'll marry the man."

"Who knows?" Hilary said with a touch of lightness. "Kevin and I are in no rush to decide our future. We're simply enjoying the present." She shifted, drawing her feet under her so that she sat curled in the chair. "Now that your basic question is answered, Logan, will you be so kind as to take yourself off?"

"There are one or two other points we should go over before I leave," he said carefully. "Not the least of which is the fate of any competitors in a situation like this one."

"What situation are you referring to, Logan?" Hilary demanded, feeling more uneasy than ever.

"A situation in which I'm willing to take what I want and to hell with the competition," he said succinctly.

"I thought you didn't care for the violent approach," she snapped back, her face aflame at his implication.

"I'm sure you'll have too much sense to allow the issue to develop to the point where physical force is necessary."

"You and my father both seem to think I'll stop short of provoking you or any other male to violence," she said grimly, recalling Crawford's comment that morning. "I suppose I should be flattered by your belief in my levelheaded approach to life but somehow all I can conclude is that both of you think I'm going to be easily intimidated. Well, my father, at least, should know better. And you, Logan Saber, should have had enough experience in the business world to recognize determination when you see it. I've told you once and I'll tell you again. I will not marry for the sake of a business transaction!"

"Which brings us to my next point," Logan interjected easily, just as if he didn't realize she was on the verge of throwing something at him. "You will be marrying me, Hilary Forrester. And while I don't care at all about your past romances, I should make it quite clear that there will be no more. Whatever is going on between you and Kevin Thorne will have to come to an end. Once acquired, Hilary, I do not share my holdings with any other man."

He got to his feet with an unexpected swift, graceful movement which left Hilary, open-mouthed with shock, staring up at him. Quite casually he leaned over and hauled her up beside him.

"How dare you, Logan Saber!" she managed to breath, conscious of his fingers on the brilliant scarf at her throat. "How do you *dare* talk as if you're going to get what you want from me! I wouldn't marry you if . . ."

"Please, Hilary, don't say anything you'll have to take back later. As a first-rate cook you ought to realize how unappetizing it is to have to eat one's own words!"

"Shut up and get out of here this instant . . ." she began forcefully, supremely aware of how much stronger he was.

"I do like this scarf," he said, his fingers still toying with it. "I find myself unable to resist discovering if it indicates what I think it indicates."

A split second later Hilary found herself swept against him in a crushing embrace.

Chapter Three

Hilary's initial reaction to the unexpected shock of Logan's kiss was astonishment. Astonishment at the sheer power and force of it and astonishment at the very idea that a man would even try such a passionately aggressive tactic with her of all women! Certainly none of Crawford's other candidates had taken this approach!

But even as such thoughts raced through her startled brain, Logan was moving to consolidate his position. One large hand traced the contour of her back until it came to rest possessively at the end of her spine. With a determined pressure he arched her against him.

"Logan!" she managed once before his mouth covered hers, taking ruthless advantage of the parted lips to investigate the warmth of her.

"Stop struggling," he ordered in a harsh whisper as his other hand held her head still. She felt his strong fingers at the back of her neck and knew, instinctively, that although he wasn't hurting her, she would be unable to break free.

"Can't you see that I want you?" he demanded gratingly, his mouth moving along the line of her jaw to the tip of her earlobe.

"What you want hardly matters," she gulped, her hands pushing uselessly against the muscles of his chest, a fluttering in her pulse making her feel weak. What was this man doing to her? "Logan, let me go!"

"Not yet, little queen," he growled, his teeth closing with a tiny, almost stinging nip around her earlobe. "Not until you understand me a little better!"

"Understand you!" she echoed, confused by both his words and what she was terribly afraid were the beginnings of her own response. The heat of his passion seemed dangerously contagious. Of their own volition, her hands moved from his chest to settle first on his shoulders and then, as he responded with an even more possessive hold, her arms circled his neck.

"That's right, honey," he told her as strong fingers curved along her hip, seeming to enjoy the shape of her. "I want to make certain you understand that I want you. I've wanted you since the day you walked into my office, announcing yourself as my future wife! So regal and yet so sweet . . ."

"You mean you want my father's restaurants," she snapped, trying to resume her struggles and finding herself too thoroughly trapped.

"Damn the restaurants!" he muttered.

"I . . . I don't believe you," Hilary wailed. "You're as greedy as all the others. Ouch!" she added as he tightened his arms around her until she could barely breathe.

"If you want to think I'm marrying you for the restaurants," he snarled, lifting his head slightly to glare down into her bemused eyes, "go ahead. It won't change anything in the end. It will only prolong matters!"

"Prolong them to the point where you'll decide the game isn't worth the effort?" she shot back, goaded.

"You won't succeed in managing that, honey," he told her, a hint of a ruthless smile touching the corner of his mouth. "Do you know," he went on almost musingly, "I really didn't come here tonight with the intention of making love to you . . ."

"Good!" she interrupted fiercely, "Because you aren't going to be allowed to do so . . ."

"I had planned to restrain myself," he went on as if she hadn't spoken. "I wasn't even going to kiss you quite yet. I knew you'd be somewhat resistant to the idea. But then you had to go and make it clear you thought yourself content with your artist friend. It suddenly made me very determined to let you know just how much I want you. I know there is a lot of passion in you. All I have to do is tap it. Make it respond only to me. . . ." His mouth came back down on hers with a fierceness that was startling. She was overwhelmed.

The next time he lifted his head, Hilary found herself gasping for breath, unable to understand her reaction. His words hammered in her brain. He'd called her passionate! Told her he wanted her and kissed her with a level of desire she had never known from other men. Was she really capable of generating those feelings in him? . . . No! the rational part of her mind screamed. It was all a trick! A new tactic to win her and the restaurants. She must not let herself be fooled. But passion was turning out to be a heady thing, indeed.

"Something tells me your artist friend will soon be looking for a new bedmate," Logan announced, the male satisfaction clear in his deep voice. "You're not going to be content with him again, Hilary Forrester. And I have no intention of letting you try to find with him what you've just found with me." The lids of the brilliant gray-green eyes lowered until he was watching her with a curiously menacing expression.

"What . . ." Hilary licked her dry lower lip and tried again, demanding in a small, defiant tone, "What makes you so sure it's not even better between Kevin and me?"

"So you admit that what we just experienced was good?" he asked silkily, throwing her into utter confusion.

"Oh, you! That's not what I meant at all and you know it!"

"Nevertheless, I'll be happy to answer your question," he said, a flashing grin crossing his face. "It's simple, really. You're too surprised by your own reaction. If you'd known such sensations before, you wouldn't find yourself so startled. And don't bother denying that you're taken back by the whole thing, honey. Your feelings are quite plain in those beautiful eyes. Can you honestly tell me you want to go back to a lukewarm affair with Thorne?"

"Yes!" she snarled, lying through her teeth and not caring in the least. "He, at least, doesn't treat me as if I were a . . . a thing to be possessed! And I know for a fact he doesn't want Crawford's restaurants!"

"You're determined to be difficult about this, aren't you?" Logan sighed, shaking his head in a small gesture of resignation.

"You're absolutely right I'm going to be difficult!" Hilary gasped. "Beginning right now!" With that she drew back a sandal-clad toe and kicked him in the shin. A childish effort, she admitted at once to herself. But she had so few weapons at her disposal and besides, the results proved enormously rewarding.

"What on earth . . ." Logan released her immediately, stepping backward and grabbing automatically for his injured leg. "You little devil," he began, massaging his shin for a moment before straightening and starting toward her in a threatening fashion. "I ought to take you over my knee and wale the living daylights out of you!"

"What?" she retorted scornfully, holding her ground. "Is that the best you can do? I'm crushed! After that passionate little love scene? After all that garbage about being able to make me feel sensations I've never been privileged to experience before you happened into my life? So much for the passionate lover, I guess. Surely a genuinely passionate man who adored and desired me would not find himself in your position within seconds of devastating me with a mere kiss?" Hilary spoke fast, knowing she had to score her points quickly. Logan showed every evidence of being quite willing to resort to brute force.

The momentary anger faded from his expression as Logan eyed her consideringly, not touching her. Slowly a rueful grin curved the corners of his mouth as he stood contemplating her, his hands on his hips.

"It does sort of ruin the image, I'll admit," he returned easily.

"Definitely," Hilary nodded vigorously. "The fact that you find yourself kicked in the shin by the woman who is supposed to be melting in your arms and you respond by threatening to spank her leaves us with a whole new insight into the situation. We must conclude that either I wasn't swept off my feet after all or . . ." she let the sentence hang suggestively.

"Or?" he prompted interestedly, one bushy mahogany brow lifting.

"Or," she said smoothly, "You're not quite the passionate lover you thought yourself to be. Perhaps both conclusions are correct!"

"You weren't swept off your feet?" he queried with a mocking look of disappointment.

49

"Of course not," she assured him, her chin lifting proudly. "What woman would kick the man who had lifted her to the heights with only a kiss?"

"A woman who was afraid of putting herself in that man's power?" he offered softly, eyes gleaming.

"Only a man with an incredibly inflated ego could come to that conclusion!" Hilary told him with an edge of sheer disgust in her tone.

"Or a man who badly wanted it to be the truth because he, himself, had been swept off his feet," he countered in his dark, velvety voice.

Hilary stared at him, uncertain how to react to his further teasing. "Let's not go back to your original contention that you really have fallen for me," she finally said bitterly.

Logan watched her intently for a moment and then lowered his gaze to the pattern of the carpet beneath his feet as if deep in thought. Finally he spoke, not looking at her. "It's obvious you're not going to buy that particular line tonight . . ."

"Or any other night," she supplied, her words bringing his eyes back up to meet hers. Hilary wasn't at all sure she understood the expression which flickered in the gray-green pools. If she allowed herself to dwell on what it might mean, she knew she would become a little frightened. And no man had ever really frightened Hilary.

"You may rest assured I'm not going to stand here all night and keep repeating that I want you!" he muttered.

"Then we're accomplishing something, at least!"

"But I'm giving you fair warning, sweetheart. The fact that you have a few nasty habits like kicking me in the shin at inappropriate moments, isn't going to save you from me. Nor is Kevin Thorne going to be able to

50

protect you. I know what I felt when I held you in my arms. There is a fire in you, Hilary Forrester, that I want to own completely and I don't care one bit about any of the things that stand in my way: The restaurants, Thorne, your stubbornness."

He was good, Hilary thought dismally. Very good. He'd found a weakness in her that none of the other candidates had even suspected. A weakness she couldn't fully describe.

"Since I don't believe your feelings for me are real, you're going to have a hard time convincing me to marry you," she told him bravely. "And even if you did persuade me that you desire me, that still wouldn't be enough reason to marry you. I think I explained in your office, Logan Saber, that when I marry, it will be for love."

"And, naturally, since you don't believe I really want you, you aren't about to believe that with me the wanting is all wrapped up with the loving, are you?" he asked whimsically.

"No!" What did he think she was? A complete fool?

"Okay," he conceded softly. "I'll abandon that approach altogether. It's hard on my ego, anyway!"

"I can imagine!"

"We'll try it another way," he went on smoothly; too smoothly.

"What are you talking about?" she demanded, frowning severely.

"If you don't choose to believe I want you then I must convince you that you want me," he said simply, the gleam in his eyes flaring brighter.

Hilary swallowed at the audacity of the man, eventually finding her tongue. "Not a chance, Logan Saber! If you think I'm so weak-willed that . . ."

"Not weak-willed, honey," he corrected with a slow

drawl, "On the contrary. It's your willpower that's complicating everything so much! I give you my word, I'm not underrating it. You may be one efficient businesswoman, Hilary, but there's no way on earth you can match my experience in dealing with difficult opponents. I'm eight years older than you, remember?"

"Those years of experience aren't going to help you one bit!" she swore furiously.

"Good," he nodded approvingly. "I'm glad you're seeing the matter in the light of a challenge. This way I won't have to worry about you running away."

"I never run from a problem!" she said haughtily, her pride touched.

"Now that we've established that you are, one, not afraid of being outgunned by a more experienced businessman and, two, not the sort to run from a situation, you shouldn't have any objections to proving your abilities, should you? Have dinner with me tomorrow night."

Hilary's eyes blinked in surprise at the sudden invitation. He had slipped it into the conversation so neatly after first making her stand on her pride.

"No thank you," she began formally.

"Afraid?" he taunted with a small chuckle that succeeded in angering her further. For the first time in her life, Hilary told herself, she was finding out what it felt like to be pushed into recklessness!

"I'm not afraid, I just don't relish the idea of spending an evening having to kick you in the shins in order to avoid being pawed!"

"I guarantee not to force myself on you, honey," he said immediately. "You'll only get as much lovemaking as you want. I give you my word I'll call a halt as soon as you tell me to do so. Any other objections? Or do you just want to admit you're scared to death of a simple evening out with me?"

It was the final shove needed to push Hilary over the edge. "I'm not in the least scared of you! . . ."

"Prove it!"

"All right! One evening and that's it! Will that satisfy you? Prove I'm not in a trembling heap at your feet?" she snapped in a fury.

He relaxed visibly, looking more than satisfied. Hilary instantly regretted her words but it was much too late. They both knew it.

"If I can't convince you to trust me for a second date after tomorrow night, I'll have only myself to blame," he smiled.

"You won't accuse me of being afraid?" she mocked.

"No. You have my word. If you don't enjoy the evening, I won't use your pride against you to get another date."

"I was a fool to let you do it the first time," she admitted, her temper cooling rapidly.

"Look at it reasonably, sweetheart," he advised consolingly. "I had to make a major concession in order to get you to go out with me. Think of the deal as a compromise."

"You consider it a major concession to allow me to call a halt if I feel you're getting obnoxious?" she demanded, her sense of humor beginning to reassert itself as the whole atmosphere in the room lightened. She knew it was Logan who was responsible for a change in the mood. He was now in a much less formidable role, apparently content with winning a mere date from her. How much of the aggressive embrace earlier had been designed to make her think of a date with him as a way out of a dangerous situation? It was all so confusing, Hilary told herself unhappily.

"You've made it clear you don't think much of my lovemaking," he retorted sadly, "But do you have to resort to labeling it obnoxious?"

Hilary, feeling more in charge of the situation by the minute shrugged with patent disinterest in his battered ego.

"Hardhearted Hilary," he murmured ruefully. "Well, to answer your question, yes, I do think of letting you handle the reins in a matter involving my, er, obnoxiousness, as a concession. A hell of a concession, in fact," he finished briskly.

"It will only be for one evening," she grumbled consolingly. "I'm sure you'll survive with your ego intact."

"You don't believe it's going to be difficult for me to keep my hands off you, do you?" he asked wonderingly, walking slowly across the room to glance out the windows. One strong hand raked through the thickness of his hair as he stood with his back to her. If she hadn't known better, Hilary told herself, she might almost believe he really was going to find it hard to follow her lead and avoid any lovemaking.

"You're not the first candidate who thought he could bowl me over with a kiss!" Just the first one to almost succeed, she added silently.

"You're telling me my fate is destined to be the same as that of the other three?" he inquired wryly, still focusing his attention on the view.

His stance gave Hilary an unobstructed view of broad shoulders and narrow waist. She remembered the strength of his embrace and knew a small shiver at the thought. There had been so many factors impinging on her senses during the moments of his kiss; the clean, bracing scent of his aftershave, the heat of his body, the hardness of the muscles in his thighs as he held her against him. . . . Determinedly she took a grip on her wandering emotions. A man like this didn't fall in love with a woman like her. He'd want someone like Julia. A beautiful, reckless, dashing female. The fact that Logan Saber wasn't as classically handsome as most of Julia's men wouldn't hinder him in the least, Hilary acknowledged. Logan would be more than capable of holding his own in any contest for Julia's favors!

Why was she thinking of Julia at this moment? Deliberately Hilary eyed her midnight visitor and said, "The other three were rather relieved to be out of the running by the time they had to quit the field, Logan. You'll probably feel the same." Unfortunately, the last sentence didn't come out quite as bracingly as she might have wished. It had almost sounded faintly regretful, she thought angrily.

"Don't put me into the same category as the other three candidates," he warned, rounding on her with unexpected abruptness. The alarming expression she had seen before was back in the depths of his eyes although there was no threat in his attitude. "I'm my own man, Hilary Forrester, and you'll only be fooling yourself if you continue thinking of me as just another candidate. There is a vast difference."

"A vast difference?" she mocked. "Well, you are larger than the others," she admitted thoughtfully.

"The better to hold you, my dear," he countered with a distinctly wolfish smile.

"And you may be a little brighter than the others," she conceded wryly. "None of them managed to trick me into a date so easily after I'd realized what was going on!"

"I imagine it was you who did the maneuvering," he told her, the smile widening. "But I didn't exactly trick you. I merely managed to salvage something from a rapidly deteriorating situation!"

"You needn't bother looking pleased. I'm on my

guard now," she retorted spiritedly, thinking that one night out with Logan Saber wasn't going to be so bad. As long as she controlled the evening's events what harm could there be in having dinner with him? She'd enjoyed the lunch in Los Angeles . . .

"Yes, ma'am," he said humbly. "By the way, your salt cellar collection is excellent. I studied it before you came home this evening."

"What?" Hilary peered at him, momentarily confused by the change in topic.

"Your little salt bowls," he explained politely, indicating her display case. "That's a particularly nice swan. Cambridge Glass Company, isn't it?"

"Well, yes, it is. Thank you," she said automatically, thinking she had somehow missed the turning point in the conversation. "I found it at a shop in the San Francisco Bay Area. She had a number of good pieces that had just come in from an estate sale . . ." Hilary broke off with a rueful smile. "Do you have a lot of success with that strategy?" she inquired deliberately.

"What strategy?" he asked innocently.

"Keeping the opposition slightly off balance? I'm only just beginning to realize how you work it," she grumbled.

"I don't understand, honey. If you're referring to my mention of the salt cellars, that was nothing but a change of conversational topic."

"Change of topic, my foot," Hilary complained. "You know damn well you've run the gamut from passionate lover to clever businessman to casual conversationalist in the short time since I've walked into this room. No," she held up a hand to ward off what appeared to be another protestation of innocence. "Please don't explain!" Privately she decided she would have to be very cool and very careful around this

56

man. He had succeeded in keeping her one step behind him most of the time she had known him. In addition to being annoying, however, it was also a bit of a novelty for Hilary.

"What time are you going to pick me up tomorrow night?" she inquired, determined to do a little topic changing, herself.

"How about six-thirty?" he suggested promptly. "Your father gave me the name of one of your favorite restaurants in town."

"I'll bet he did." Hilary's mouth twisted downward for a second. "Anything to help the cause."

"He really does mean well, honey," Logan said softly.

"I know he does. That's one of the things that makes it so difficult to get out of these situations he sets up! At least in your case everything's out in the open. He knows you've been warned. You know you've been warned. This time I'm not playing any games!"

"Good," he applauded cheerfully, coming toward her a couple of steps and then stopping again as her braided head lifted warily. He surveyed her appraisingly. "I don't mind games, you understand, but it will simplify matters if you're not going to invent any."

"You think that leaves the field open for you?" she demanded archly.

"Yes," he retorted simply. "As it happens, I'm well up on game theory. I find it very useful in business."

"I can imagine," she snapped waspishly, thinking that the comment had told her more than he probably wished her to know. It reinforced the knowledge that he considered her, essentially, a business matter.

"But for every encounter there are a few basic rules . . ." he went on, his soft drawl dropping to a deeper, warning note.

"Not if your opponent isn't playing!"

"In this case, my opponent will play by them or take the consequences," he advised calmly.

"Don't bother giving me a list of rules for your game, Logan Saber. I don't have any intention of concerning myself with them!"

"They're simple enough," he half smiled. "You shouldn't have any difficulty remembering them. Actually, they can all be boiled down to one. While you and I are in the process of resolving our little differences, some might say while I'm courting you . . . yes, I thought you'd get a chuckle out of that, you're not to continue your affair with Kevin Thorne."

Hilary's amber gaze narrowed at the forceful note in his voice. They had returned to the conversation's starting point, it seemed. Well, she had no intention of being bullied. He was an intriguing man in spite of his mercenary interest in her and she was willing to go out with him once under the conditions that had been established. But he mustn't get the idea that he could warn her off other men.

"I'm not going to stand here in my own living room and engage in a shouting match with you," Hilary told him loftily. "If you want to retain the privilege of taking me out tomorrow evening, you had better stop issuing orders about matters which don't concern you in the least!"

He studied her for a moment, as if deciding how much he could push her before she rebelled completely and refused to go out with him at all. Hilary could almost see the thought processes and hid a triumphant smile. True, she would have to stay on her toes with this man, but she could handle him!

"Such a haughty little thing," Logan said mildly, although the expression in his eyes said something a lot more forceful. "I suppose we'd better continue this conversation tomorrow night. You're obviously just looking for an excuse to back out of the evening and I don't intend to give it to you."

"My date with you will come to an end tomorrow night the moment you introduce your warnings and rules into the discussion!"

"Perhaps when Thorne finds out you're seeing me, he'll take the initiative and call off your tepid little romance! Are you going to tell him about tomorrow evening, Hilary?"

"Kevin and I do not account to each other for every hour of our lives!"

"Not even every night?" Logan asked blandly.

"We have an understanding," Hilary announced with a fine air.

"Very modern," he approved. "I guess I'm a little old-fashioned in that respect, however. Don't expect to have such an understanding with me, sweetheart."

"I don't expect to have a serious relationship or understanding with you at all!"

"Which only goes to show that life is full of surprises. Even at our ages!"

"You're incorrigible," Hilary groaned. "You must go through a lot of women if you treat them all like this. How long does it take before they get fed up with the rules and regulations?"

"Actually," he drawled carefully, "Most of them tend to hang around until I stop paying the bills." He moved another pace or two closer. Hilary began to feel as if she were being stalked.

"And you've decided to find one who will bring a dowry, is that it?" she countered scornfully, instantly chiding herself mentally for letting the knowledge hurt her.

"I hadn't thought of it in quite those terms, but, yes, you will bring me a valuable dowry, Hilary. I don't imagine you'll believe me if I tell you that it won't consist of the restaurants," he said softly, shortening the distance between them still further.

"You're right. I won't." Hilary contemplated moving backward at the same rate he was advancing. Unfortunately, that smacked of cowardice. Besides, this was her home! She decided to make another bid to gain control of the conversation.

"I think it's time you left, Logan," she declared firmly, eyeing him challengingly. "You've got what you came for. I hope you enjoy your evening out tomorrow night but, frankly, I'd think it would be frustrating sitting across the table from the source of the several restaurants and knowing you won't get them!"

"Think how much pleasure you'll have taunting me with them," he pointed out drily.

"That's an idea," she shot back enthusiastically. "I could string you along, make you think you were going to get exactly what you had bargained for with my father and then, wham! No Hilary and no restaurants. Sure you still want to go out to dinner?" she added hopefully.

"I'll take my chances," he growled, reaching for her. Hilary didn't attempt to escape the hand on her shoulder, contenting herself with a ferocious frown.

"If you're thinking of kissing me again," she said distinctly. "Forget it. I'm claiming tomorrow night's privileges as of now!" She faced him bravely, wondering what she would do if he didn't back down.

"Give a woman a little power," he grinned ruefully, "And it goes straight to her head!" He gave her a gentle shake. "Why don't you admit you're as intrigued by me as I am by you? You would never have agreed to go out to dinner with me otherwise and you know it!"

"The old ego talking again?" she asked with mocking sweetness, wondering privately if he wasn't right. He fascinated her in some strange way; a way none of the others had come close to managing.

"I'll be lucky if there's anything viable left of my poor ego by the time you've finished with it, honey," he sighed, releasing her abruptly as if her shoulder had grown uncomfortably hot under his hand. "I guess I'd better go along with your kind advice and leave. If I stay much longer I'm liable to lose control . . ."

"And wind up making mad passionate love to me?" she snapped scathingly.

"No," he returned smoothly, starting past her on his way toward the door. "Wind up doing what I almost did earlier, paddling you!"

"Come now," she chided almost cheerfully as she followed him down the short hall. "You're a businessman, remember? You're supposed to use your silver tongue and your brilliant strategy against me, not brute force."

"I'll use whatever looks like it has a chance of working, Hilary honey," he warned, turning back to face her, one hand on the doorknob. "You've already admitted I'm bigger and brighter than the other candidates, so you'll have to be very careful, won't you?" The expression on his face was a rather daunting combination of determination and hard ruthlessness. It lasted only an instant until Logan seemed to realize it wasn't a very politic expression under the circumstances and replaced it with a smile.

But Hilary had seen it and the unease she had experienced before during the evening returned in full force. The thought that she might be playing games that were a little too advanced occurred to her.

"Goodnight, Logan," she said haughtily. "I'll see you at six-thirty tomorrow night."

"Yes," he agreed, "You will. And, Hilary," he added, pausing once more before going through the door. "You won't lose your nerve and run off will you? I'd hate to be put to the trouble of having to find you. . . ."

"I've told you, I'm not in the least afraid of you, Logan Saber!" She glared at him, disliking the way he had of making her pride work against her, but, at the same time, half admiring his maneuvering.

"Good." Logan slammed the door, taking with him the excitement, warmth and tension which had filled the room while he was in it.

Hilary stood contemplating the closed door for several seconds after he had gone, a curious thought running round and round through her brain. It was a while before she allowed herself to recognize it and when she did, Hilary immediately mocked herself for it. It was simple, really. When Logan had warned her not to run off because he didn't want to have to bother finding her, she had wanted to ask him if he actually would have done just that.

Would he go to the trouble of chasing after her and begging her to return? Hilary thought of all the implications of such an action on a man's pride. It would surely be a humiliating experience for a man like Logan Saber. Well, she wasn't likely to discover the ultimate results of running away from him. Hilary realized she had her own ego to worry about and fleeing from a man like Logan would be extremely hard on it. It would be an admission that she couldn't handle him, she decided and knew, even as she said as much to herself, that it would also be an admission of something else, something she did not wish to recognize at the moment . . .

Thoughtfully she made her way through the cozy house, turning off lights, pausing to glance once into the salt cellar case and then making her way to bed. She tried hard to concentrate on the work she had decided to accomplish the next day. There was a definite satisfaction lately in doing her books for the restaurant. Nothing was as satisfying to a businessperson as a clear, clean profit. But even that pleasing thought wasn't enough tonight to drive memories of her visitor out of her head.

Hilary undressed in the brightly-decorated bedroom with its red and gold bedspread and the Chinese prints on the wall, her mind full of Logan Saber. It wasn't until her head finally touched the pillow and she had drawn the patterned sheets up around her chin that she finally admitted the truth.

She had blamed Logan for maneuvering her into a position where she could hardly refuse to dine with him. But the reality of the situation was that she very badly wanted to spend an evening with the annoying, irritating and, yes, exciting man.

Chapter Four

Monday morning, Hilary treated herself to a walk on the beach before tackling her financial books. It was still quite early as she parked the car on the street and strolled, barefooted, across the expanse of white sand down to the water's edge. The sparkling beaches were one of the main drawing attractions for the town, luring countless tourists during the warm seasons. Many of those tourists, Hilary had discovered, were sufficiently affluent to warrant stocking some very exotic wine in the Silver Salt Cellar's collection. The two evenings a week on which the restaurant served dinner a special effort was made to provide the clientele with out-of-the-ordinary culinary delights. The people who ordered such food were willing to pay for it and the wine to accompany it.

She ought to be sleepy, Hilary decided as she walked. By the time she had finally rid the apartment of Logan, it was quite late. But somehow, her main feeling this morning was one of anticipation. Sternly she told herself she ought to repress any interest in the man, but that was turning out to be one of those things easier said than done. What was it about him that attracted? He wasn't as good-looking as the other candidates although, presumably he was as successful, if not more so. His clothing was more conservative. The brief glimpse she'd had of the car the previous evening told her he didn't drive one of the exotic sports models favored by the last three would-be suitors for her hand.

No, she was skirting the issue, Hilary told herself deliberately, frowning into the distance as she gazed out to sea. The simple truth of the matter was that Logan was the first of the candidates her father had turned up who attracted her not only on a physical level but on an intellectual one. Being in an honest mood there on the beach in the early morning light, she forced herself to acknowledge that there was a curiously intriguing undercurrent to their conversations. It had, on the occasion of their luncheon together, become almost comfortable when they had discussed their mutual interests. When the talk became bantering, or, as it had at times last night, challenging, the undercurrents generated a rare excitement.

The frown narrowing Hilary's amber gaze became darker as her thoughts flew to the way she had felt when Logan had kissed her. She reminded herself that he was a clever man. He must have reasoned that men, in general, seldom bothered with the arrogantly passionate approach when dealing with a woman like Hilary. They were far more likely to try an intellectual or casually sophisticated angle. Some, like Kevin, found her easy-going independence a relief after dangerous, clinging women. Her automatic insistence on equality in her relationships probably deterred any who might have been tempted to try sweeping her off her feet.

But Logan had decided to make the attempt and she

found herself surprised by the degree of success he'd already had. There was a strange feminine satisfaction in allowing oneself to think she had a potent effect on a male. Was this the feeling Julia experienced when she conquered one man after another? Hilary wondered if she could find a way to ask her.

But in the meantime she was playing with fire, Hilary decided grimly. She was turning out to be unexpectedly vulnerable to Logan's particular attack and the wisest course of action would be to refuse to see him. Perhaps she would do exactly that after tonight. . . .

Once she'd settled down to work in the little office she maintained at the back of the restaurant, the time rushed past. When she finally looked up from the accounts several hours later, Hilary was startled to find that it was nearly one o'clock. With a sense of satisfaction, she closed the ledger in front of her and tidied the desk. Success was gratifying when one had worked so hard for it. Even her father was quite proud of her. That thought made her think, guiltily, that she really ought to call Crawford and invite him over for dinner sometime during the week. Of course, he'd probably take that as a sign that he'd been forgiven for introducing yet another man into her life! She was about to walk out the door when the phone on the desk rang.

"Hello, Kevin," she said, recognizing his greeting. "How's the commercial art coming along?"

"Brilliantly, if I do say so, myself. You know, there's a lot less pressure doing this kind of stuff. I might make a habit of it! It should be ready for you to view Wednesday morning. How about me picking you up bright and early so you can see it in the good light? I'll make sure you get home in plenty of time to make it to the restaurant before it opens."

"Okay, but you don't have to pick me up, Kevin. I can drive to your place . . ."

"I don't mind. Besides, I owe you a ride, remember? You're the one who drove me to the film the other night."

Hilary laughed. "All right. See you Wednesday morning. Was that the main reason you called?"

"Art first, naturally, but I also thought you might like to know Melanie called this morning," Kevin said with an attempt at lightness.

"Oh, Kevin," Hilary breathed, "Did she really? Did she say anything encouraging?"

"She said she's coming back to Santa Barbara," he told her, trying to sound calm, but Hilary could hear the excitement in his voice.

"I'm so glad," she replied honestly.

"Not half as glad as I am," Kevin chuckled. "This time things are going to be different!"

"You mean this time you'll find room for her as well as painting in your life?" Hilary asked promptly.

"I've learned a lot from you, love. You've helped me see that the business side of life isn't all bad and I think I've outgrown my 'artistic temperament,' thanks to the way you kept laughing at me whenever I tried to indulge it!" Kevin said wryly.

"Maybe you've just grown up a little," Hilary smiled into the phone. "It happens to some of us!"

"Whatever the reason, this time Melanie's going to stay! I won't let her go again." There was a depth of passion in his words that told Hilary Kevin spoke the truth and she wished him the best. It struck her with uncomfortable relevance as she hung up the phone that the reason her own relationship with Kevin had never progressed beyond the friendship stage was obvious. There had never been any passion in his voice when he spoke to her; just as she'd never experienced any consuming passion for him.

It was, perhaps, unfortunate, that thoughts of such a wild and reckless thing as passion kept whirling through Hilary's head all afternoon. As she dressed for her date with Logan she lectured herself severely on the difference between passion and love. Surely there was a difference and she must not lose sight of it!

Standing in front of a mirror, Hilary coiled the long braids around her head in the familiar, neat coronet, her mind busy with the problem of what to wear. She was placing the final pin in her tightly wound honey-brown hair when the doorbell rang. Surprised, she glanced at the clock, saw that she had another forty-five minutes before she should expect Logan, and went to answer the summons. The long green robe flirted about her ankles as she flung open the door inquiringly.

"Logan!" she squeaked, startled. "What are you doing here? It's only a quarter to six!"

"I'm aware of the time," he assured her drily, standing very tall and very solid on her doorstep. He was dressed in a well-cut sports coat toned to go with equally well-cut slacks. Both were in shades of brown and perfectly complimented by a soft yellow shirt and dignified tie. The richness of his hair gleamed damply from a recent shower and, Hilary took an unconscious whiff, he smelled good! Some compound of aftershave, soap and pure male.

"Do you mind if I come in and wait for you?" he asked politely, seeing that she was still standing there, staring at him.

Hilary jumped, hastening to open the door further. "No, of course not. I just wasn't expecting you so soon. You strike me as being the type who is always on time for appointments; never early or late," she added with a small grin.

"I don't suppose you'd believe me if I told you I couldn't wait to start the evening?" he asked, gray-green eyes gleaming down at her as he brushed past into the hall.

"No," she agreed readily, shutting the door. "But it's a good line. Will you fix yourself a drink while I finish dressing? Everything's in the kitchen on the right-hand side. I won't be long."

"Take your time. Now that I'm here, I'm not in any hurry," he told her easily, heading immediately for the kitchen. Hilary stared after him, perplexed, and then scurried into the bedroom.

Sometime later she emerged to find Logan standing on the veranda, admiring the view in the darkening late spring light. He turned almost immediately as she came through the living room, a warm smile of approval shaping his mouth.

"Very nice," he congratulated, hoisting his glass in mock salute as his eyes traveled leisurely over her figure. "All restrained elegance except for the wild, heathen necklace. I like that." He came forward slowly until he stood in front of Hilary. "You look good in green and gold, sweetheart," he added, referring to the deep emerald shade of her simple, close-fitting sheath dress and the dazzling ornateness of the gold necklace at her throat. He deliberately took a sip out of the glass he was holding and then held the crystal rim to her lips. "Have a drink," he ordered softly, leaving her little option unless she wanted to risk spilling the contents down the front of her dress.

Her eyes locked with his, Hilary obediently sipped from the glass, her nose wrinkling at the harsh taste of the Scotch. The gesture of insisting that she drink from his glass seemed possessive in a way she couldn't explain, but she couldn't think how to make an issue of it.

Her compliance seemed to satisfy Logan, however. He took the glass away from her lips and downed its contents before setting it on a nearby table.

"Terrible stuff," Hilary murmured in an effort to lighten a situation which had suddenly become too charged.

"The Scotch?" Logan glanced idly at the glass and then back to her. "You shouldn't keep it around, if you don't like it," he smiled.

"I keep it for the occasional visiting executive," she retorted drily. "It's either that or have to learn to mix martinis. Don't you know those are the only sorts of drinks good businessmen appreciate?"

"Judging by the fact that the Scotch bottle was only half full, I think you're entertaining too many visiting executives," Logan said, his voice a soft growl. "We'll have to put a stop to that. There's only one visiting executive I want drinking from that bottle."

"Are you going to be difficult tonight, Logan?" Hilary queried interestedly, her head tilted pertly to one side as she studied him. "Because if you are . . ."

For an instant the gray-green eyes hardened and Hilary had to stifle an impulse to take a precautionary step backward. Then Logan smiled. A deliberate, persuasive smile.

"I'll make a deal with you," he said almost blandly.

"A deal?"

"Umm. You promise to make an effort to enjoy yourself tonight and I'll . . ." he paused and then concluded bluntly, "I'll try very hard not to act as if I own you."

Hilary stared at him, wondering if he were serious. But he was! She could see the willpower he was exerting just to make his ridiculous promise. Unable to help herself, she burst into delighted laughter.

"Oh, Logan," she managed, "You're impossible!"

"Does this mean you're willing to relax and enjoy this evening?" he demanded, some of her humor reflected in his eyes.

"Why not?" she shrugged lightly, feeling quite reckless. "You're paying for it and I haven't had a sophisticated evening out since the last candidate." She turned toward the door. "Are you ready to go?" she tossed back over her shoulder.

"I'm the one who's supposed to ask that," he told her drily, moving to take the shawl she was removing from the hall closet. "Trying to control the evening right from the start?" he added, his teasing smile containing a hint of warning as he draped the light material over her shoulders.

"Definitely," she grinned unrepentantly. "It's my evening, isn't it?"

"Not entirely," he returned, holding the door open for her. "I consider myself equally involved."

"But we did agree I would be in charge," she reminded him smoothly.

"Only in a limited capacity," he corrected.

"I'll bet you're a difficult man to work for," Hilary said with a chuckle as they started down the steps toward his car parked at the curb. "Do you let your managers have any real authority?"

"Only as much as I think they ought to have. Thinking of applying for a position?"

"Never!" Hilary shook her head immediately, a small laugh still gurgling in her throat. "I don't think I could ever work for anyone. I'm much too independent. Unless, of course, I could get a job with an enlightened executive who would give me complete freedom to go my own way. . . ." she amended, slanting a glance up at Logan as she slipped gracefully into the front seat of the car.

"You mean someone who would let you get away

with murder?" he clarified interestedly before shutting her door.

"Something like that."

He grinned, closed the door and walked around to the driver's side.

"You won't find me that indulgent," he told her, starting the engine. "At least not in most areas. I'll be happy to give you your head in purely business matters, unless what you want conflicts with good sense . . ."

"You mean unless it conflicts with what you think makes good sense," she put in demurely.

"Exactly. But when it comes to the, shall we say, *personal* side, I think I'm destined to be a very possessive, um, employer. I'll watch you like a hawk," he finished, a thread of steel underlying the banter.

"You sound as if you're using the term employer as a euphemism for husband." Hilary said in mock innocence.

"Weren't you?" he said equally mockingly, glancing at her out of the corner of his eye as maneuvered the car away from the curb.

"Nope. Don't get any ideas, Logan. I'm going out with you tonight partly because I don't have another date and partly because I went out at least once with all the other candidates."

"But you *are* going to enjoy yourself?"

"Hopefully," she said pertly.

The evening had begun well enough Hilary decided a short time later as they shared a small, intimate table in the lounge of the restaurant Logan had selected. Certainly it was several degrees above the evenings she had spent with the other men her father had turned up during the past year. She told herself she ought to take warning from that fact, though. It was undoubtedly much the safer course *not* to enjoy the company of the candidate who was rapidly on his way to becoming the most dangerous of the four. But Hilary's normal good sense seemed to be napping tonight. Perhaps, she consoled herself, it was because Logan had assured her she would not have to fight off his advances later. Perhaps it was something more than that. Something Hilary really didn't want to contemplate at the moment. . . .

"I see it pays to dine out with a locally known restaurateur," Logan remarked as several members of the restaurant staff greeted Hilary and cast a curious eye over her escort.

"It's the next best thing to being a known overtipper," Hilary said, amused. "Believe me, I make certain the owner of this place gets excellent service when he lunches at the Silver Salt Cellar!"

"There's a lot to be said for running a small business where one gets intimately involved," Logan mused, sipping at his drink and watching Hilary as she tasted hers.

"I like it, but I'm sure it's nothing compared to the satisfaction you get from doing business on a much larger scale," she smiled, lowering her lashes in an attempt to hide the mocking look in her eyes as she deliberately flattered him. To her surprise, though, he took the comment seriously.

"It's *been* satisfying," he stressed in a slow, thoughtful tone which caused her to raise her eyes immediately. "But now I'm not so sure . . ."

Hilary frowned, uncertain if this was some new tactic. Was she supposed to feel sorry for the poor rich businessman?

"Are you trying to tell me you no longer thrive on the challenge of high-powered business?" she inquired politely.

"It has its moments," he acknowledged. "But, to put it simply and I know I'm leaving myself wide open to

73

one of your periodic forays against my ego, I've accomplished what I set out to accomplish. I can keep building what I've got, but . . ."

"Ah hah!" Hilary grinned, helping herself to a handful of peanuts. "A classic example of the Crisis of the Thirties."

"I beg your pardon?"

"Don't worry. It's perfectly normal, according to a book a friend insisted I read last month." She leaned forward enthusiastically. "You are in your thirties, aren't you?" At his bewildered nod, she continued. "You see at your age a person has either achieved the ambitions of his twenties or he's failed. One way or another it creates a crisis period during which people start looking around for other answers. For some that means building on what they've already got, as you just suggested. For others it means finding something new with which to challenge themselves." Hilary relaxed back against her seat. "Lecture ended. Sorry I can't be of further help but, unfortunately, the book didn't have answers to each individual case."

"Thank you, Dr. Forrester," Logan said wryly.

"No charge. What will you do now that I've identified the underlying problem?"

"Solve it," he retorted easily.

"Really?" she asked interestedly. "How? Go back to L.A. and build a bigger empire? Minus Crawford's restaurants, of course?"

"No," he drawled slowly. "I think I'll proceed along the lines I started developing the day you showed up in my office."

"What lines?" she demanded at once.

"I'll tell you someday. I don't think you're predisposed to give my plans a fair hearing at the moment."

"Meaning they involve me? Well, just keep in mind

that the Crisis of the Thirties is only one of many you've got to look forward to."

"There's one for the forties?"

"And every few years after that. My father, for example, went through a major one ten years ago after my mother died. That's when he set out to live the great Southern California executive lifestyle. The only difference between him and the younger candidates he's produced for my hand is one of degree. I expect you'll gravitate in the same direction."

"Minus a few restaurants?" Logan added, one brow lifting.

"Minus a few restaurants," Hilary confirmed.

"Fascinating. Now that we've successfully analyzed me, let's start on you. Fair's fair, you know. What will you do when you hit the Crisis of the Thirties?"

"Open a new restaurant, perhaps," she retorted flippantly.

"Do you see yourself married by then?"

"Possibly," she said more cautiously.

"Not a business marriage, naturally, but a sweet, gentle affair based on equality and respect?" he persued deliberately.

"I've told you I intend to marry for love . . ." she began a little heatedly and was forced to halt the discussion as the waiter came forward to tell them their table was ready.

But, although Hilary would have been content to let the subject drop, Logan wasn't. As soon as the business of selecting the meal and the wine was out of the way, he returned to the topic with a determined air.

"Okay, you've convinced me you're going to marry for love or not at all but you haven't convinced me that you're going to recognize the love that's right for you, Hilary honey." He sat back and smiled at her. "How will you know it when it appears? You'll be so busy looking for someone who fits your inner image of what you think constitutes a good mate that you'll probably ignore the real thing."

There was such an expression of bland smugness on his features as she waited for her response that Hilary knew she was being set up for a fall. The only question was what kind of a fall?

"I'm sure I'll recognize love the way one normally recognizes such things . . ."

"A feeling of rightness?" he suggested teasingly.

"Well, yes. Wanting to be with the other person; wanting to share. A willingness to tolerate imperfections in the other. Interests in common. All sorts of clues," she wound up staunchly.

"So far what you've described is a good friendship and I'll buy that as far as it goes. But one shouldn't marry friends, Hilary, not even if one sleeps with them."

"Why not?" she challenged, fighting down a wave of color at his obvious reference to Kevin Thorne. "Friendship seems like a good basis for marriage to me!"

"You're leaving out the factor necessary to make the relationship a love affair."

"What's that?" she frowned ferociously.

"Passion," he told her softly, a deep, seductive twist in his words.

"You mean lust," she hissed, feeling herself redden further beneath the intensity of Logan's lazy gaze.

"No, I mean passion. I'm old enough to know the difference, Hilary honey."

"Don't call me that," she ordered, clutching at straws.

"Don't change the subject," he replied readily. "If you're honest you'll admit we already have the elements of a good friendship. I know you're not ready to admit that there's a passion between us, but you will . . ."

"Logan!" Hilary pleaded, horrified by the possibility that someone in a neighboring booth might overhear and equally horrified that there might be a grain of truth in what he was saying. At least on her side. There was no denying the charged atmosphere which existed between them when they argued. Nor could she deny the element of excitement in just being near the man. He was undoubtedly accustomed to having women go crazy like this, she berated herself furiously.

"Don't worry, honey," he said gently, the look in his eyes softening as he took in her expression. "I'll behave myself."

"I should hope so," she snapped, picking up a fork to attack her salad. "I was hoping to enjoy the evening!"

"You will," he promised. "But perhaps it's time we turned to a less volatile topic."

"That would be fine with me!"

"Eat your food like a good girl and I'll show you how charming I can be when I set my mind to it," he grinned cheerfully.

And he did prove it, Hilary had to admit much later. Logan turned the conversation first to salt cellars and then to her restaurant business. From there they went on to politics, the effects of inflation and a discussion on the poor nutrition in business lunches. But no matter how prosaic the topic, Hilary was never allowed to forget that she was in the company of a man who wanted her. The underlying excitement Logan managed to weave into the conversation had an incredibly weakening effect. By the time dessert arrived, Hilary found herself questioning the fact that Logan's desire for her was based entirely on the restaurants.

She allowed herself to be persuaded into going from

dinner to a nightclub, telling herself there was really no harm in pretending for one evening. It was rather like playing Cinderella. . . .

"I've been looking forward to this since I picked you up tonight," Logan murmured, guiding her onto the dance floor and taking her firmly into his arms.

"Dancing with me?" she queried, surprised and a little flattered.

"A socially sanctioned opportunity to hold you close," he elaborated, suiting action to words. With one hand he guided her head down onto his broad shoulder. Hilary, after only a token resistance, decided the middle of a dance floor was not the place to take a stand. And besides, he had a very comfortable shoulder.

The rosy glow in which she seemed to be moving through the evening was shattered some time later, however, when a throaty, feminine voice interrupted the conversation with Logan. The small table Hilary had been sharing with her escort had seemed a hidden island retreat until that moment. She glanced up, immediately recognizing the owner of the sultry tones.

"Hello, Julia," she said quickly, aware of Logan shifting his attention to the newcomer. Hilary's contentment with the evening dissolved. Beautiful, reckless, glamorous Julia was here and suddenly reality came crashing back.

"Hilary, don't tell me Crawford's found you another one!" The lovely, slanted eyes moved with open appraisal over Logan.

Wincing inwardly, Hilary spoke rapidly, "Julia, this is Logan Saber. Logan, Julia Fane."

"The reckless blonde, I believe," Logan said with an ease Hilary could only admire. After that crack Julia had just made! Out of the corner of her eye she watched her escort get politely to his feet. Julia's eyes gleamed as she took in Logan's height and build.

"Reckless?" the lovely blonde questioned musingly, holding out a polite hand. "Well, perhaps, if the goal is worth it. . . ." Her expression left little doubt that she found Logan eminently worth her attention. But, then, Hilary reminded herself, Julia habitually looked at every man like that. "You don't appear to be the type of man who's frightened of reckless blondes, however, Mr. Saber."

"Which only goes to prove how appearances can be deceiving, Miss Fane. The truth of the matter is I'm terrified of them. They can be so wearing." He gazed down at Julia with polite blandness, ignoring the acres of shapely cleavage on display.

Hilary couldn't help feeling a bit warmed by Logan's obvious lack of response to the other woman's lures, but Julia didn't appear in the least daunted. She laughed delightedly and reached up to touch Logan's cheek with a long nailed hand.

"I'm sure we could find something to do that wouldn't be overly taxing," she smiled invitingly. "Hilary," she added, not waiting for a response from Logan. "You will feel free to call on me again if you need help in handling this one, won't you? He'll be a much more interesting assignment than the last. I won't even demand a free meal at your restaurant in exchange! Well, I've got to run. Dear Conrad is waiting for me. Hope we meet again and soon, Mr. Saber." She made her departure on a sultry laugh and a cloud of expensive perfume, the daringly cut gown floating around her provocative figure.

For an agonizing moment Hilary could find nothing to say. She couldn't even bring herself to look at Logan. It seemed easier to concentrate on the half-empty contents of her glass. It was Logan who broke the silence.

"You must have a real streak of ruthlessness in you to turn an unsuspecting male over to *that!*" he announced drily, his words succeeding in bringing Hilary's eyes up to meet his. To her surprise there was laughter in the gray-green gaze.

"Well, you know how it is," she said carefully, relieved that he seemed able to laugh at the situation. "Business is business . . ."

"Tell me, does everyone in town know about the candidates?" he demanded, shaking his head ruefully.

"Most of my friends do." Hilary lifted one hand in a helpless gesture. "Let's face it, when Hilary Forrester started showing up in various local night spots with a series of sophisticated, charming, rich men, it needed an explanation!"

"I expect your friend Thorne was in the forefront of those demanding the explanation?" Logan suggested in deceptively neutral tones.

Hilary peered at him sharply, uncertain of his mood now. "Kevin knows my father's candidates mean nothing to me," she said, belatedly remembering her intention of using Kevin as a shield.

"He must be extraordinarily liberal-minded to allow you out with one man after another, even if you haven't been interested in any of them so far. Doesn't the man realize the risk he's running?" There was a probing tone in Logan's voice now that went deeper than the question he had asked. Hilary shifted slightly to hide a moment's nervousness. Did he suspect already that her relationship with Kevin with a red herring?

"Kevin's a very modern male," she said with false airiness. "He's an artist, remember? He sees things differently . . ."

"Differently, perhaps, but not necessarily more clearly," Logan corrected coolly.

"What is that supposed to mean?" Hilary asked pointedly.

"Only that he's known you for about a year and he still hasn't seen the real Hilary. The man must have no artistic sensitivity whatsoever not to have discovered the warmth and passion hiding behind your charming businesswoman facade. But that's fine with me," Logan continued quickly as Hilary opened her mouth to protest. "Being a naturally greedy man, I'm very happy to find out he hasn't had the sense to lock you away from the world."

"Logan, if you're going to go on like this, I'm . . ." Hilary began, feeling flustered and wishing she hadn't had that last drink.

"Relax, honey," he soothed, capturing her hand in his larger one as it moved with small agitation on the surface of the table. "You're still ultimately in charge of the evening, remember? There's no need to panic."

She frowned but could think of nothing to say. He was right. She was the one in control tonight. Why was she letting herself get so upset? Taking a firm grip on her nerves, Hilary tried a deliberately lofty smile.

"I'm not in a panic, but I would appreciate it if you would refrain from talking to me as if you had some sort of . . . of rights over me! You'll ruin the evening!" she lectured.

"I have an idea," he grinned engagingly. "Let's blame this on Julia. Things were going beautifully before she appeared on the scene. Let's say it's all her fault that we got on this subject, okay?"

Hilary hesitated and then gave in with a small smile. "All right. I'll go along with that. There's no point in spoiling the rest of the evening, especially since it's

81

going to be the only one we have together," she concluded firmly.

Something flickered briefly in the gray-green gaze and then disappeared. Whatever it was had lasted long enough to send a warning to Hilary's common sense, but for the life of her she couldn't imagine why her wary brain had reacted to it. She was in no danger from this man, unless, of course, she allowed herself to be charmed off her feet and she certainly had no intention of losing her self-control to that point!

"I don't intend for this to be our last evening together, Hilary," Logan said gently, so gently she almost didn't hear the underlying growl in his voice.

Hilary watched him narrowly for a moment, suddenly aware of the fact that there was a great deal of the evening left to get through. If she was going to be the one who called a halt when he made the inevitable pass later at her front door, why was she feeling rather like a kitten in the presence of a lion? She wasn't a weak female to be easily swept off her feet by a charming and sophisticated man. She'd already proved that three times during the past year! Why was Logan Saber turning out to be such a threat to her peace of mind?

Chapter Five

At two o'clock in the morning Hilary finally slid out of the emerald sheath, removed the exotic necklace and tumbled into bed only to frown at the darkened ceiling until she abruptly realized what had happened. Logan Saber had done it again. With a wry smile curving her mouth, Hilary swore lightly and snuggled into the bedclothes. That man had an uncanny ability to keep her guessing! She had to admit she'd been outmaneuvered again. Not only had there been no opportunity to put a grand halt to his lovemaking efforts, he'd also left with her promise to join him for dinner the next evening.

There was nothing like expecting a man to make a heavy pass at one's door and getting only an affectionate kiss dropped on one's forehead to throw a woman off stride, Hilary decided grimly. She supposed it was the surprise of his mild-mannered goodnight that had made her agree to the date the next evening. When he'd asked her she'd been so busy wondering why he wasn't sweeping her into his arms that she'd responded without thinking.

But then, she thought ruefully, what risk could there be in dating a man who was determined to act the gentleman? He might have tried a real kiss or two, Hilary sighed a little sadly.

In spite of the unexpectedly disappointing climax to the previous evening, Hilary found herself looking forward to Tuesday night with happy anticipation. The routine of the Silver Salt Cellar was a familiar and soothing background for her straying thoughts. It was a good thing that the business of running the restaurant had long since been reduced to an efficient, smooth process because there were definitely moments in the day when her mind was not altogether on her work.

Hilary managed to carry out the planned experiment with the new scone recipe before the close of the day and she remembered to conduct the audit of the wine cabinet but when she finally locked the door and headed for her car, her thoughts were on what to wear for the evening ahead.

Her second night out with Logan began as interestingly as the first. When she opened the door for him at six o'clock he stood waiting with a small package in one hand, his eyes sweeping over her appreciatively.

"No flowers?" she teased, taking the little box happily and tearing off the ribbon.

"I thought you might prefer that," Logan answered, wandering over to the cabinet where he'd found the Scotch the previous evening.

Hilary, one part of her mind noting that he was helping himself to her liquor supply as if he felt quite at home, lifted the box lid with a sense of excitement. The package was the right size and shape to be a salt cellar and it was.

"Oh, Logan!" she breathed, delighted. "It's beautiful!" She cradled the little cranberry-glass salt bowl in her hand, holding it high to examine the exquisite workmanship of the delicately footed silver frame.

"You like it?" he asked, leaning against the counter and sipping his Scotch while he watched her admiring the gift.

"Like it! It's gorgeous!" she exclaimed, "and so unusual, too. I don't have another that's even similar."

Logan said nothing, merely smiling as she turned away from her examination of the salt cellar and met his eyes. For an instant she hesitated, aware of the waiting quality of his expression and then she smiled back.

"Thank you, Logan. . . ." And then, touched by the thought that he'd spent the day searching out the beautiful gift, Hilary stepped forward very quickly stood on tiptoe and kissed him softly on the cheek. He didn't move as she retreated instantly. To cover the flush she felt rising into her face, Hilary suddenly became very busy with the wrappings.

"I'll put it into the display case," she said chattily, moving across the room to the salt cellar cabinet. "And then I'll be ready to go . . ."

"No hurry," he said quietly behind her, but Hilary was finding the living room had become rather close quarters with Logan Saber dominating it. She moved quickly to get her shawl, aware of his silent approval of her severely cut black dress and the outrageously huge hoops of her earrings.

"You look more like a little pagan queen than ever tonight," Logan announced as he held the door for her. "It's a miracle some man didn't carry you off over his shoulder years ago!"

Hilary, who thought she looked her usual, sedate self, but appreciating the flattery, grinned.

"Probably because I've made certain that any man who contemplated it would have to be prepared to pack along my business records. Men tend to lose some of their romantic inclinations when a woman makes it clear she expects to work hard at making a success out of herself."

"Don't think you'll be able to intimidate me that easily," Logan smiled with a touch of menace.

No, Hilary thought with a pang. Your shoulders are broad enough to handle a woman and her career baggage, but is that really what you want? Is is possible you could truly want *me?* Or are we just playing games?

Dinner was every bit as enjoyable as it had been the previous evening and Hilary found herself doing less verbal fencing. The conversation flowed as easily, at times lightly bantering, but it seemed more relaxed. That goodnight peck on the forehead had had its effect she decided with an inner smile at one point. Logan Saber had an instinct for putting her off guard. Or perhaps he just had an instinct for handling women. Sobering thought.

But when she went into his arms on the dance floor an hour later, Hilary stopped pondering her reactions and gave herself up blissfully to the throb of the music and the feel of Logan's strong arms around her.

"You're a pleasure to dance with, Hilary," Logan whispered into her coiled hair. "A pleasure to hold in my arms. I'm glad," he added with outrageous whimsy, "that we have no deal about who's got what authority tonight!"

"What's that supposed to mean?" Hilary demanded, pulling back slightly to meet his eyes with what was meant to be a quelling glare. Unfortunately, Logan spoiled the intended effect by chuckling and hauling her back tightly against him.

"Relax, little queen. You know I would never do anything you didn't want. . . . Oh, no!" he concluded abruptly, not sounding particularly angry, but not sounding terribly pleased, either.

"What's wrong?" Hilary was aware Logan's attention was focused behind her.

"Nothing really. Your father just walked in with a party of friends. I guess we'd better say hello."

"Crawford? Here?" Hilary glanced over her shoulder in time to see her father's tall figure disappearing behind a row of potted plants.

"Maybe it's just as well," she smiled. "I ought to invite him over for dinner and now is as good a time as any to ask him. If he can fit me into his busy schedule, that is! In fact, I owe you both meals," she added, smiling. "How about tomorrow evening?"

"It's a deal. Provided I'm not expected to share you with Crawford all evening!"

"Knowing him, he'll have plans for after dinner that don't include us. Who got back to the cottage first last night? You or him?"

Logan grinned. "I heard Crawford come in about an hour after I'd hit the sack. How did you guess?"

"I know him. Come on. Let's go say hello." Hilary turned, leading the way across the dance floor, Logan at her heels.

"After which duty, I think we'll make our departure," he commented behind her. "I prefer not to do my courting under the eagle eye of your father. It's bad enough having to share the cottage with him . . ."

"Logan!" Hilary chided, embarrassed as they neared the rows of plants shielding the booth Crawford and his friends were occupying. "I wish you wouldn't . . ." she broke off as Crawford's rich tones fell clearly into one of those small silences that can strike a room.

"So I told the young man I'd give him his pick of the restaurants, including the one that's making all the money down in Orange County if he succeeded in marrying Hilary. I think Saber's the one who can do it, too. Got a mind like a steel trap and enough willpower to match my daughter's. They'll make a . . ."

Crawford's voice went on, hidden now by the increasing volume of noise in the room, but Hilary didn't need to hear any more. She was standing stock still on the other side of the greenery, chilled to the bone.

It was the depth of that chill more than anything else which told her how close she had come to disaster. How close she had come to falling in love with Logan Saber. Even as she stood there, telling herself over and over again that she had no reason to be shaken; that she had known the truth all along, Hilary realized that in an incredibly short time she had come too close to a perilous edge. She wanted nothing more right now than to flee to some lonely spot where she could berate herself for her stupidity and perhaps release her anger in tears. Without thinking, she half turned away, only to come up against Logan's hard frame. His arms went around her.

"Well?" his voice sounded grating and harsh as she automatically tried to disentangle herself from his grip. "Are you going to cause a scene by running out the door? Or shall we finish our business with Crawford like the adults we supposedly are?"

Hilary lifted an amber gaze drenched in fury and pleading.

"Logan, I can't . . . I won't . . ."

But Logan's response was to meet her gaze with a hard, gray-green one which contained all the implacable challenge of the sea during a storm. His hands propelled her forward, around the edge of the potted plants until they stood in full view of Crawford and his friends.

Hilary, given little option but to deal with the

situation now that it was upon her, felt a wave of cold anger coming to her rescue as she listened to Logan cordially greeting Crawford, explaining that Hilary had wanted to invite both himself and her father to dinner the next night. She could tell by the rueful expression in her father's eyes that he knew she'd overheard his last remarks. She watched him get to his feet and come away from the table to greet her.

"Hilary," Crawford whispered as he leaned down for her dutiful kiss. "I'm sorry, please believe me . . ."

"It's a pity you didn't finish the rest of the story, Crawford," Logan said with quiet grimness, his hand still gripping Hilary.

"You mean the part about how you told me to go to hell after I'd made my grand offer? Sorry, you must have arrived too late. I told that part first!" Crawford glanced down at his daughter who smiled back coolly, her expressive eyes gleaming with a rage unlike anything she had ever experienced.

"Please don't bother trying to salvage the story for my benefit," she said with a saccharin sweetness, wondering if anyone could possibly guess what it was costing to keep the cool little smile in place. Out of the corner of her eye she saw Logan studying her intently and realized with a jolt that he would know how much effort went into the task. Unconsciously her chin angled a fraction higher. It had been close, very, very close, but she'd found out the truth in time. Rather, she corrected herself mentally, she'd had it confirmed.

"Logan and you both know I'm aware of the business games being played. When all parties know the rules the chosen victim really isn't in that much danger, is she? I sent the first three packing, didn't I, Crawford? I'm sure I'll be able to handle Mr. Saber, also." She refused to meet Logan's eyes, but the strong hand anchoring her arm became almost painful and she knew she wasn't going to be allowed to pull free and walk away in regal splendor. Better not to cause a scene by trying it.

"Hilary," Crawford began determinedly. "You've got it all wrong, dear, I . . ."

"Your guests are waiting, Crawford," she reminded him.

"Yes," he agreed resignedly. He hesitated and then asked carefully, "Is the invitation for tomorrow night still on?"

"Hardly," she began, the temper simmering just under the surface beginning to show. "I'm sure you'll understand . . ."

"We'll be there at six-thirty," Logan interrupted brutally, turning to Crawford. "Don't worry, I'll take care of her tonight. You'd better get back to your table."

Crawford met Logan's eyes in a man to man look which left Hilary totally out. "Yes," the older man finally said thoughtfully, nodding his handsome, silver head, "I think you are the one who's going to take care of my daughter. If you survive the next few hours, that is!" The last words were added with an abrupt, masculine smile which drew an answering, rueful one from Logan.

"See you tomorrow night, Hilary," Crawford said swiftly and Hilary, who was madly formulating plans to be out the next night, said nothing.

She continued to keep silent until it became apparent that Logan had every intention of reseating her at the small table they had been using earlier.

"Please take me home, Logan," she said stiffly, refusing to accept the chair he was dutifully holding.

"Why?" he demanded, meeting her eyes bluntly. "How has anything changed? You claimed you knew the facts all along."

90

"Knowing I'm part of a business deal and having that information announced to the world in a cocktail lounge are two different things!" she snapped. "I want to go home. If you won't take me I'll call a cab. Or Kevin," she added spitefully. The last drew a quick response.

"I've told you you're not going to see Thorne again so don't go making rash statements," Logan grated. "Don't worry, I'll take you home if you're certain it's what you want . . . ."

"It is!"

"Keep that in mind," he told her enigmatically, collecting her shawl from the back of the chair.

Hilary refused to look at him, sweeping toward the front door of the lounge with an angry stride. Never had her temper been so fully aroused.

"Don't you think you ought to ask yourself why you're so furious, Hilary?" Logan suggested softly, holding the car door for her.

"I've told you . . ." she began seethingly, flashing a simmering glance up at him as she got into the vehicle.

"I know, but I don't believe you." He closed the door with a small slam. A moment later he slid in beside her, his large frame making the car suddenly seem very confining. Hilary felt a shaft of unease. He was so big, so much stronger . . .

Grimly she took a hold on her stirring imagination. Logan was a civilized man. He wouldn't hurt her. She certainly had nothing to fear from him. After all, he would have to answer to Crawford. There would be no restaurants . . .

In spite of the reassurances to herself, the silent drive back up the hill to her home had never seemed longer. Hilary wanted so badly to be alone to ask herself how she could have come so close to being taken in by a smooth-talking businessman. She refused to think about what might have happened if she hadn't over-heard her father's comments. What if she had become even more enmeshed in Logan's spell before confirm-ing the truth? And spell was what it was, she reminded herself sadly. Even now when she should be experienc-ing nothing but loathing for the man the uppermost thought in her mind was how wonderful it might have been if matters were different.

Logan, who had made no further efforts to break Hilary's self-imposed silence, parked the car in front of her condominium and swung open his door.

"There's no need to see me inside," Hilary told him bitterly as she quickly extricated herself from the car and started up the walk. "Why don't you go back to the lounge? Crawford, I'm sure, will be happy to entertain you along with his other friends!"

"Because I have some unfinished business with you," he began in his soft, gritty voice.

"Business!" she echoed furiously. "That's all you can think about, isn't it?"

"A bad choice of words," he conceded with a small smile which reminded Hilary of nothing so much as a knife blade. "Let's just say I have my own plans for this evening."

"If those plans include me, you can just forget them!" she said, trying unsuccessfully to free herself from the grip on her arm. Did the restaurants mean so much to him that he was going to try and convince her that Crawford really hadn't made a bargain? Did he think she was so stupid? So vulnerable?

"Hilary, I know you're upset, but we have to talk . . ."

"Why?" she demanded, fishing in her purse for her keys. "There's nothing more to discuss."

"Why not? I want to hear you admit the truth!" he said in a tone that was almost a snarl. For the first time

Hilary sensed that Logan was more than disgusted with the failure of his plans. There was an anger in him that was beginning to make itself known. An anger which might very well more than match her own. The unease she was feeling deepened.

"I've already done that. Or rather my father did it for me," she said bravely, setting the key in the lock and hoping the trembling in her fingers didn't show.

"No, you see, you haven't. The reason you're so angry, Hilary Forrester, is because you were beginning to fall in love with me and I'm not leaving tonight until I've made you say that much, at least!" he exploded with a controlled violence that was thoroughly alarming.

"No!" she breathed furiously, stepping quickly through the door. "I was merely going along with the game until it ceased to be amusing. Tonight it stopped being interesting. I'm quitting the field, Logan!"

"But I'm not playing games, Hilary," Logan informed her, flinging out a formidable hand to catch the door and hold it open as she attempted to slam it shut in his face.

"Leave me alone!"

"Not tonight," he vowed, the look of utter determination in his eyes making her swallow nervously.

"Logan, you can't . . ." Hilary felt the door thrust out of her hand and she backed away, trying desperately to decide how to handle this man who had chosen to invade her home. He was a businessman, for God's sake! Not some primitive, all conquering hero. So why was she feeling like an embattled princess?

Logan closed the door behind him with an unnatural care, his eyes never leaving Hilary's defiant gaze. In the hall light he seemed quite massive, quite capable of slinging a woman over his shoulder and making off with her into the night.

Hilary took another grip on her imagination. What was the matter with her? She could deal with this man. She must deal with him! Drawing herself up to her full height, Hilary lifted her head challengingly, refusing to move backward as he came toward her.

"If you're thinking you can assault me and get away with it, I've got news for you, Logan Saber," she bit out. "When my father finds out you so much as put a hand on me without my permission he'll ruin you!"

"I'm not going to rape you, you little idiot," he told her, the curve of his knife-blade smile still on his mouth, the gray-green eyes gleaming. "I'm going to make love to you. And the only thing you'll tell your father afterward is that you want to marry me."

Hilary stared at him an instant longer, recognizing the power of his intention and finding it more frightening than if he had threatened her with physical harm. She remembered her unwilling response the last time he had held her in his arms and knew with a sinking sensation that he could probably overwhelm her once again. Even now, when she ought to be screaming in fear or searching for the fireplace poker, Hilary felt the strange excitement rising in her, spreading out to her fingertips until she seemed to tingle all over with it.

The instinct to challenge him was not so much a desire to fight him off, she realized with a painful gasp, as it was to make him prove how much he wanted her. But that was ridiculous! It wasn't her he wanted, it was the financial reward she could bring him! She must stop confusing the two. But when he looked at her like this, with a hypnotizing, warm and masculine need swirling in the depths of his eyes, it became very difficult to think logically.

In mounting confusion and panic, Hilary stepped backward, putting out a hand in a warding off gesture.

Logan ignored it, pacing her as he shrugged easily out of his jacket. His hand went to the knot of his tie.

"Why don't you at least have the grace to admit that it's my father's restaurants you really want. Not me!" she hissed, knowing suddenly that she wanted him to deny her accusation. The tie was unknotted now, dangling from his hand. Hilary realized she was halfway across the living room. Her present path would take her out onto the veranda where she would be trapped.

"I'm not going to admit it because it wouldn't be true. It's you I want, Hilary, and before tonight is over you're going to confess that you want me, also!" The promise on his lips was duplicated in his eyes and in the whole, lean length of him.

"Even if you . . ." Hilary stumbled as a wave of color surged into her cheeks, "Even if you succeed, you needn't think I'll marry you!"

"You think I'd settle for a casual affair like the one you've been enjoying with Thorne?" he inquired, closing the distance between them. "Not a chance. You're going to belong to me and that means a ring on your finger and the same bed—my bed—every night. You've made it clear you don't feel particularly bound to a man just because you share his bed on occasion, so with me you'll go the whole route . . ."

"I won't . . .!"

Logan's hand holding the tie moved with unexpected swiftness. The strip of silk fabric circled around Hilary's outstretched wrist, tightened with a jerk, effectively chaining her.

She stared in astonished fury, first at the binding tie and then at Logan. She could hardly believe this was happening!

"How do you *dare?*" she raged in a voice so full of

anger and some other passion she could barely speak above a whisper. Instantly she raised her other hand to free herself but with a small motion Logan used the tie to yank her off balance so that she stumbled against him. She knew she was trembling with the force of her emotions. Emotions that seemed to run the gamut from a strange female fear to a heated excitement.

"I dare because I want you," he said simply, one hand holding taut the silk bond around her wrist, the other circling to pull her tightly against him. "I was going to give you time. Let you adjust and find out what it means to desire someone the way I desire you," he told her, his dark voice a hoarse growl as he lowered his head so that his mouth was within inches of her own. "But you had to go off in a rage tonight and, frankly, I don't have the patience to rebuild everything Crawford managed to tear down with his stupid comment."

Wide-eyed and knowing she was trapped both by his strength and the curious weakness generated by her emotions, Hilary waited for his kiss. Above all else right now she wanted to believe the passion in his eyes. Never had a man looked at her with such naked wanting and never had she experienced such a tumultuous need. The combination was dynamite.

And then his mouth was covering hers in a deep, disturbing kiss that further ignited the smoldering flames within her.

This couldn't be happening, Hilary thought frantically, her body almost painfully aware of the effects of Logan's marauding mouth. Not to her! This sort of thing was probably routine for Julia Fane but it certainly wasn't for Hilary Forrester! The mild romances she had experienced in the past disappeared as if they had never existed. Nothing had ever been like this.

"Logan!" she gasped as his lips left her soft mouth to

trail a string of kisses down her throat. "Why me? I'm not . . . I'm not like Julia. You can't expect me to believe you've gone crazy over someone like me!"

"Tonight I'll show you how crazy I've gone," he whispered. "Don't you know how intriguing you are with your proper, businesslike little ways spiced with all the hints of underlying passion? My God! I still can't believe that fool Thorne hasn't taken more pains to guard his treasure!"

"Kevin isn't . . ." she began helplessly, enthralled with his seductive words. She had been going to tell him that Kevin wasn't her lover, but he interrupted, his fingers pushing back the collar of her dress to expose her shoulder.

"Kevin isn't important any longer," he grated. Maintaining his hold on the scrap of fabric around her wrist, he thrust his other hand into the neatly woven crown of her hair, ripping loose the careful braids.

"I knew it would be like this," he said with deep male satisfaction as the honey-brown hair spilled across her shoulders to her waist. His fingers raked lovingly through the braids, tugging until her hair was a thick, waving mass. "Did you think I didn't know what you were hiding with your hair all neatly bound up? Did you really believe I was so blind I couldn't see all the hints you were throwing my way?"

Desperately Hilary tried to regain some control. She was a mature woman, not a gullible teenager. She knew what really lay behind Logan Saber's passion.

"I won't be seduced by one of my father's business associates," she stormed, aware of how vulnerable she was, praying he wasn't equally aware.

"But, Hilary honey," he murmured, his fingers on the zipper of her dress, "That's exactly what's going to happen. Although I will admit that there's a question as to who's seducing whom!"

Summoning all her will, Hilary made a last effort to free herself, lashing out at Logan with her unbound hand, but he deflected the blow easily and then, before she could recover, he swept her up into his arms.

Startled anew, Hilary's own arms instinctively went around his neck in an attempt to steady her reeling senses. She closed her eyes to make the room stop spinning, but opened them immediately as Logan made a low, rumbling sound of amusement deep in his throat. When she met his eyes he was gazing down at her, a half-smile playing at the corner of his mouth, gray-green eyes glinting with a fire that was laced with humor.

"I've always wanted to do this," he told her striding across the room.

"What?" she asked helplessly, not understanding.

"I've always wondered what it would be like to sweep a woman off her feet and carry her into the bedroom, her long, soft hair flowing down over my arm," he explained obligingly.

"Oh!" Hilary managed, realizing she ought to be struggling but unable to do so any longer. Logan's tie still dangled symbolically from her wrist. She attempted one last verbal sally, but it was weak and she knew it.

"You mean this isn't your usual approach to women?" she demanded scathingly.

"No," he assured her, his eyes narrowing as he kicked open the door to her room and stepped inside. "I'm a businessman, remember? My usual approach is far more businesslike. The truth is," he went on, setting her down gently on the red and gold bedspread in the darkened room, "I've always dreamed of finding a woman who was capable of arousing all the passions in me. A woman," he continued in his deep, mesmerizing voice, "who could make me want to protect her,

98

admire her, tease her, talk to her, beat her, shower her with gifts and carry her off to the bedroom!"

"Logan, listen to me," Hilary began desperately, feeling like a captured slave girl sprawled in a heap on her master's bed. A slave girl who was foolishly trying to use reason as a weapon against a man who held all the available power.

"Do you suppose," Logan went on as if she hadn't interrupted, his fingers at work on the buttons of his shirt, "That all of us superficially sedate business types are secretly harboring this inner core of romantic passion?" He tossed the shirt onto the floor with a low laugh and threw himself down on the bed beside Hilary. "Or is it only you and me?"

Hilary tried to shake off the hypnotic effects of the unreal situation and edged across the bed, but one strong hand reached out immediately to wrap around her narrow waist. She stilled, knowing there was little fight left in her. The unfamiliar level of passion Logan had unleased was demanding further exploration and satisfaction.

Logan's kiss was a continuation of the one he had started in the living room, but this time Hilary lay tangled in his arms, her legs trapped by the weight of his thighs, her wrists held captive above her head in one of his hands.

"Logan, I don't . . ." she whispered, breathlessly, feeling strong, probing fingers slide the unzipped dress down across her shoulders, revealing the lace and satin of the outrageously expensive bra she had bought once on a whim. He maneuvered the dress to her hips with a determined tug.

"Don't talk, Hilary," he ordered gently as his lips went greedily to the soft swell of her breasts. "Not unless you're ready to tell me all I want to hear." He undid the clasp of her bra and Hilary gasped as his hand moved possessively to trace the shape of her.

"That's it, little one," he husked against her skin as she arched involuntarily against his hand. "Let yourself go. Let me feel the flames in you. I want both of us to get burned!"

The heat of his large body was irresistible. Hilary was suddenly pressing closer, demanding more of him and when he released her wrists she flung her arms around him, her fingers digging into the skin of his smoothly muscled back.

It couldn't be real she thought as his caressing lips elicited a soft moan from her. Deliberately she trailed her hands down Logan's spine, glorying in the exclamation of desire the action drew from him. No it couldn't be real, but the temptation to enjoy the dream while it lasted was overpowering.

"You are so lovely," Logan told her, his face buried in her thick hair. He shifted his weight until she lay totally pinned beneath him. She could sense the fire raging in his solid body and the flames in her own slender figure leaped higher to match them. "Tell me how much you want me!" he demanded as she shivered against him. "Let me hear you admit the truth about what's between us!"

"Logan, I want you!" she got out, obedient to his command. She felt him give a sigh of satisfaction. "I want you so much," she went on in a thread of a whisper. "Please, please, say you love me a little . . .!" she pleaded.

"Love you!" he repeated in a fierce tone. "My God, woman! Can't you tell how much I love you? How much I need you? Want you? I told you before it's all wrapped up in the same emotion. I can't separate out my feelings when I hold you in my arms! You're going

100

to marry me. That's all I know for certain. I'm going to have you, Hilary, all of you!"

Hilary took a deep breath, a jolting thought crowding into her bemused brain. If he loved her, even a little . . .

"Logan?" she moaned, feeling his hand on her hip and knowing there was very little time left.

"What is it, sweetheart?" he said urgently, sliding her dress off completely.

"Logan, if you love me . . . If you truly want me . . ."

"I do, Hilary honey," he vowed. "Oh, how I want you!"

"You won't . . . you won't force me to marry you," she got out in a rush. Now she would know, once and for all, how much the restaurants meant to him. "Have an affair with me, instead, Logan," she wailed softly. "Prove that you want me more than my father's restaurants!"

Chapter Six

The effect of her words was immediate and electric. Logan's head snapped up and he glared down at her where she lay pinned beneath him. The rugged planes of his face were drawn into an almost violent expression and the gleaming eyes were barely visible through narrowed lids.

"Affair!" he repeated, his voice grating across Hilary's nerves. Suddenly he seemed very heavy as he covered her softness there on the bed. "You want me to prove my love by having an affair with you? No way, Hilary. I've already told you I'm going to marry you. I'd go out of my mind trying to control you without the extra bonds of marriage. Don't you think I've learned a lesson from the way you treat Thorne? Do you think I could stand the thought of you with another man?"

"What about me? I've had to learn some lessons, too, from the previous three candidates," she whispered hopelessly. "Don't you think I have a right to find out for certain how you really feel about me? If you insist on marriage I'll never know for sure whether it's me or my father's holdings you want . . ."

"Listen, woman," he snarled, his fingers digging painfully into the smooth skin of her shoulder. "I swear you'll know exactly how I feel after tonight . . ."

"A typical male approach! You think sex solves everything, don't you? That afterward I'll be pliant and tractable?"

"You will," he agreed ruthlessly, "For a while, at least!"

"You don't sound to me like a man in love," Hilary said, her voice breaking slightly as she tried to control her emotions.

"You don't think a man can't lose his patience with his woman and still love her? I've got news for you!"

"Logan, please! Listen to me," she begged. "Everything has happened so suddenly. You've moved into my life and tried to take control as if you had a right to do so."

"Sometimes a man has to make his own rights, Hilary," he murmured more gently, his hands stroking through a heavy length of hair lying across her throat.

"Spoken like a true businessman," Hilary retorted bitterly. "That's probably exactly what the old robber barons used to say before they took over a new enterprise!"

He shrugged, his broad, naked shoulders moving slightly in the dimly lit room. "So? I appear to have the weight of tradition behind me, in that case. Come, Hilary, stop trying to reason with me and try loving me instead. I promise it will be much more satisfying!" He bent his head and nuzzled her ear, his palm moving over the nipple of her breast in a lazy, tantalizing fashion that sent another in a series of shivers through Hilary.

"Logan," she tried again, clinging to what little rationality still remained in her befogged brain. "I'd . . . I'd be faithful in an affair, if that's what you're worried about. I promise there would be no other men . . ." How could there be other men after Logan Saber, Hilary concluded silently.

"You're too independent," he told her, his hand trailing down across the vulnerable softness of her stomach, making its way much lower. "Even if I could manage to keep other men out of your life, you'd still drive me to distraction wondering where you were and what you were up to when I wasn't with you. And I have the distinct feeling you'd insist on maintaining your own home . . ."

"Well, of course," she agreed, unthinkingly.

"You see? It would never work. I want a wife, Hilary, not a mistress!"

Hilary winced at the term. "I wouldn't be a . . . a kept woman, Logan," she hissed, "Whether or not I married you!"

"Maybe not a *kept* woman," he said, and she could hear the sudden note of amusement in his voice. "But certainly an *owned* woman. You're going to belong to me, sweetheart, in every sense of the word!"

"You really don't love me at all, do you?" Hilary forced herself to say sadly. She felt him stir impatiently and went on quickly. "Oh, you may want me or you may want the restaurants. I'll never know which for certain if we marry. But I'll always know that it isn't love you feel for me. A man who loved me would prove it by agreeing to my terms . . ."

"I could easily take to beating you, Hilary Forrester!" Logan blazed, all patience gone. He was moving, rolling over to the edge of the bed and putting both feet on the floor with a thud.

Stunned at the abrupt violence, Hilary lay very still

on the exotic bedspread, her hair fanned out around her, and watched as he scrambled for his shirt. He pulled it on with casual disregard for the costly fabric and stood staring down at her as he buttoned it. There was a frightening grimness in his face which made Hilary swallow with unconscious nervousness as she met his eyes.

"I'll say one thing for you, my little bargainer, I may come from a long line of unethical business adventurers, but you sure as hell spring from an equally solid background of silver-tongued salesmen!" He ignored the cuffs of his shirt, letting them dangle open as he planted both fists on his lean hips. "God save me from women who try to make deals in bed! No, don't get up," he ordered, although she hadn't dared to move. "I'll see myself out! I hope you enjoy the rest of this evening as little as I will!"

Logan turned and stormed out of the condominium, slamming doors as he went. Hilary didn't budge an inch until she heard the front door being summarily shut. Then she very carefully undid the silk tie from around her wrist.

When the whirlwind had finally blown itself out of her home, Hilary was dismayed to find the dampness of tears on her cheeks.

The knock on her door the next morning brought an exhausted Hilary awake after only a few short hours of sleep. Logan would have been pleased to know that her night had passed in all the misery he could have wished, she thought grimly, stumbling out of bed and grabbing her robe. It had been a long time since she had cried herself to sleep and she noticed as she passed the hall mirror that it hadn't done wonders for her complexion. Her hair streamed down her back in a tangled mass and her eyes looked strained and unhappy.

Who could be pounding on her door at this hour, she

wondered, trying to pull herself together before answering the demand.

"Kevin!" she breathed, memory returning in a hurry. Cheerfully handsome, the young artist stood on her doorstep, taking in the sight Hilary presented.

"You look like you spent the night out on the tiles, young lady," he remarked, sounding surprised. "Hey, I'm not interrupting anything, am I?" He looked past her into the empty hall. "I mean, candidate number four hasn't finally made the grade, has he?"

"Kevin if you don't shut up you're going to get this door slammed in your face!"

"Hilary, what's wrong? You're not normally this vile tempered. Look, the sun is shining and I've got a fantastic piece of art to show you that is going to make a fortune for me! What more could anyone ask for?"

"A bit of understanding from one's friends! Would you mind ceasing the light banter?" Hilary demanded waspishly.

"I'm only teasing you, love. Come on, I'll make you a cup of coffee. You look like you could use it and I get the feeling you're not going to offer to make it yourself." He pushed past her, heading immediately for the kitchen. "Why don't you have a shower and get yourself into shape while I put on the caffeine? Then you can sit down and tell cousin Kevin all about it. Anything that can put you into this condition is bound to be fascinating. I'm seeing a Hilary I never suspected existed!"

"Kevin, if it weren't for the bonds of friendship and the fact that I'm in need of the coffee, I'd tell you to get lost," Hilary told him ruefully, clutching the robe around herself. "I'm afraid I forgot about our appointment this morning. Give me a few minutes and I'll be back to my usual self. I think," she amended thoughtfully as she headed for the bathroom which adjoined her bedroom.

"Take your time. It will take me a while to figure out this dumb foreign coffeemaker, anyhow. Don't you have any instant?"

"No, I don't like instant coffee. You know that. How many times have I complained about the stuff you serve me when I'm visiting you?"

Kevin made a clucking sound. "Such a vile mood. I can't wait for the tale. Hurry up with the shower!"

With a stifled groan Hilary obeyed, anticipating the feel of the hot water on her back with grim hope. Perhaps if she could get herself looking more normal, she would begin to *feel* more normal . . .

Hilary was undressed and leaning down to turn on the water when the second knock sounded on her front door. This was turning into a busy morning, she thought wretchedly, deciding Kevin could make himself useful and answer it. She didn't feel like climbing back into her robe and trying to be civil unless it was absolutely necessary. It must be a neighbor, she reasoned, pausing in spite of her intention to listen to Kevin's greeting.

There was a murmur of indistinct sound and then Kevin's voice calling out to her very clearly.

"Hilary! I think you'd better come out here! You've got a guest."

"Now what!" she muttered feelingly, flinging back on the green robe and wishing desperately she could do something about her hair. It would take ages to brush the snarls out of it, though, and Kevin's voice had sounded a bit urgent.

With a frown of annoyance, Hilary padded out of her bedroom and stopped short at the sight which met her in the living room.

"Logan!" she gasped, astounded. "What are you doing here?" She stared at him, "Let go of Kevin!" she added furiously, belatedly realizing he was holding the younger man in a rather nasty one-handed grip on the collar of Kevin's shirt.

Logan swung a glance of pure fury in her direction, his eyes sweeping over her disarrayed figure in a terrifying fashion.

"Don't worry, your turn will come next," he gritted, tightening his hold on Kevin.

"Don't you think," Kevin said in what was undoubtedly meant to be a reasonable tone, "that you ought to explain the details of our relationship, Hilary?"

"I don't need to hear the details," Logan told him, each word a chip of ice. "The only detail I'm interested in at the moment is making sure both of you understand that your *relationship* is at an end. She's mine, Thorne and she stays mine! Got it?"

"Hilary, for heaven's sake, tell him I'm not your lover!" Kevin managed, an edge of panic creeping into his words.

"I hate to spoil the drama of the moment," Hilary snapped furiously, her eyes on Logan. "But you're way off base, Logan. Kevin and I are friends; nothing more! Now let him go before I call the police!"

"Friends!" he rasped. "Is that what you choose to call it? I can guarantee you're not going to label our affair a 'friendship,'" he vowed.

"We don't have an affair!" Hilary stormed. "You walked out on me last night, remember?"

"Well, I'm back this morning and I've decided to accept your terms. The only catch is, you're going to learn that I'm setting down a few conditions of my own! First and foremost is that there will be no other men in your life from now on, Hilary Forrester!"

"Look, this is turning into one of the more eventful

mornings of my week," Kevin interrupted with a desperate attempt at lightness, "but I really think we ought to get the facts straight. To put it bluntly, man, I've never been to bed with Hilary. I swear it! I'm here this morning because I had an appointment to pick her up and take her to view my latest painting. I wanted a businesswoman's view of it because it's been done for a local business establishment. I walked in and found her looking like she does and, frankly, if you're the guy that did that to her, you ought to be ashamed of yourself! She looks like hell!"

"Thank you, Kevin Thorne, for those kind words!" Hilary turned on him, amber eyes blazing. "I ought to go ahead and let him beat you to a pulp!"

"Except that you wouldn't let an innocent man go to the wolf, would you, Hilary, old pal? Come on, tell him the truth until he listens!"

"You say you're not her lover? Then how come she let me think she was having an affair with you?" Logan demanded, but Hilary thought she detected a faint note of hope in his voice. As if he wanted to be reassured . . .

"I thought you might leave me alone if you thought I had another man . . ."

"You lied to me about him?" Logan grated, not releasing his hold on Kevin, but definitely looking now as if he wanted to be convinced.

"Yes! Kevin really is just a friend, nothing else. He's in love with a woman named Melanie, if you must know. They're going to be married soon, isn't that right, Kevin?" she added.

"As soon as I can get a ring on her finger," Kevin agreed with a rueful little smile. "And if I succeed, I owe my luck to Hilary."

"What on earth are you talking about?" Logan snapped, his eyes going back to Thorne.

"Hilary's the one who made me see I had to grow up a bit if I wanted to keep Melanie," Kevin tried a slight shrug and Logan's grip loosened somewhat. "She made me realize that I was going to have to sacrifice a little of my artistic temperament and she also made me accept the fact that there's nothing wrong in doing art for commercial reasons. A commission is a commission she said and all good artists have had them. It puts bread on the table and frees you to experiment. Hilary's been a friend and a good one, but we've never been lovers. Use your head, Saber, do you think I'd have allowed her out with you or any of the other candidates? I have a man's normal, possessive instincts, too!"

"Why, I don't know what to believe!" Logan exploded in exasperation, releasing his grip on Kevin completely and striding across the room to stand glowering down at Hilary. "Look at me and tell me one more time," he ordered, using his hand to lift her chin so that she couldn't glance away.

"Kevin and I are not and have never been lovers," she said slowly and deliberately, speaking as if he were a little slow mentally. Her irritation was plain in her voice, but she met his eyes steadily.

There was a moment's silence while Logan studied her carefully, probingly, clearly searching for something with which to convince himself. Then he relaxed visibly with a small sigh.

"Then you didn't call him to your bed last night after I left?" he said quietly, but it was more of a statement than a question. Hilary shook her head and the hand that had been under her chin moved to wrap around her neck and she was tugged against his large frame. "You don't know how I felt this morning when he answered the door . . ." Logan began, forcing her head against his chest and ignoring her attempts to resist.

"If you're trying to excuse your ridiculous behavior just now, you can forget it!" Hilary yelped, her voice muffled against the material of his shirt. She pushed against him with her small fists. "In case you don't know it, Logan Saber, you've just made a gigantic fool out of yourself! Let me go!"

"I think," Kevin said thoughtfully behind them, "that I'm an unneeded extra at the moment. Hilary, if you'll excuse me, I'll be on my way. We can schedule another viewing of the masterpiece . . ."

"Wait, Kevin . . ." Hilary tried, only to have her face pushed gently but forcefully back into Logan's shirt.

"Goodbye, Thorne. Sorry about the scene a few minutes ago, but I'm sure you'll understand," Logan said smoothly, holding Hilary tightly against him as she kicked at his leg with her bare toes.

"I think I'm beginning to," Kevin said with wry humor. "I must say you've certainly revealed another side of the Hilary Forrester I thought I knew so well. I've never seen her so . . . so unself-possessed! I thought you businesspeople were unemotional compared to us artistic types. Well, you live and learn!"

"Mmmmff!" Hilary got out against Logan's chest.

"There's just one other thing," Logan said easily, still ignoring Hilary. "Friendship is well and good but I don't want to find you here again at this hour of the morning, Thorne. Is that quite clear?"

"Very," Kevin agreed drily. "See you, Hilary!" She heard the door close behind him and Logan at last released her.

"Well, I hope you're satisfied with your big macho scene!" she snapped furiously, her tangled hair flying about as she stepped quickly away from him. "Do you go around making a fool of yourself like this fre-

111

quently?'' Hilary knew she was taking refuge in anger but she couldn't help it. She was afraid to let herself think of all the possible meanings surrounding Logan's appearance so soon after he'd left her in tears. It was easier to rail at him than beg for an explanation.

"You do look a little haggard this morning," Logan told her with an appraising glance. "Why don't you go ahead and take your shower while I finish the coffee Thorne started. We've got a lot to talk about, you and I."

"I'll take my shower when I please!" she informed him haughtily, lifting her head bravely.

"And does it please you to take it now, my lady?" Logan inquired with a hint of suggestive menace.

"Yes," she said quickly. "It does!" Hilary turned and fled back toward the bedroom.

"Hilary," he called after her and she paused at the door. "If it makes you feel any better, I did feel foolish when I realized the truth."

"Good!"

"But not for threatening Thorne," he went on deliberately, his glance warm and possessive as it swept over her. "For having let you take me in with the con game. I should have known from the beginning that you were using him as a blind."

"So score one for me!" she told him flippantly and disappeared into the bedroom.

When she emerged half an hour later, Hilary decided she was looking far more normal. Her freshly washed hair was drying in two long braids down her back and she had on a pair of close-fitting jeans and a long sleeved shirt. She took a last glance in the mirror before braving the living room and told herself she was not looking nearly so washed out as she had earlier. In fact, there was a healthy hint of color in her cheeks that definitely had not been there before Logan's reappearance. Had he really come back this morning because he was ready to meet her terms? Hilary closed her eyes briefly, gave herself a stiff lecture on the folly of raising her hopes and then opened the bedroom door.

The coffee was creating an inviting aroma from where it had been placed on the low table near the windows. Logan had already poured himself a cup and was sitting in a nearby chair, leafing through a magazine devoted to the restaurant business. He looked up as she came forward.

"Much better," he approved, studying her. "Although I have to admit I wasn't sorry to see the night had been as hard on you as it was on me. Misery loves company and all that. Here," he leaned toward the table and poured the coffee. "Have a cup."

Hilary obeyed without a word, accepting the cup and saucer and seating herself in a chair across from him. She used the excuse of stirring the dark brew as a reason for not meeting his eyes.

"So you want to have an affair with me," he began bluntly, a comment which brought her head up with a jerk. He watched her carefully as he spoke. "I take it you do still feel the same as you did last night? You haven't had a change of heart during the night?"

"No . . ." she whispered. "I . . . I haven't changed my mind."

"I'm still going to be required to prove myself, am I? Well, I won't claim to be satisfied with the bargain, but I will point out that just because I've agreed to the main terms, don't think you're going to have everything else your own way!"

"What . . . what are you talking about?" she asked nervously, not at all certain she'd taken the right course. He frightened her, sitting there and discussing the terms of an affair as if it were a business transaction. What had she let herself in for with her demand?

"We're going to conduct this affair my way," he informed her deliberately. "That means a number of rules and regulations. I can't tie you down with a ring and a license so I will have to do the best I can to achieve similar results."

"Logan, stop threatening me!" she began heatedly, not at all sure what he was driving at, but certain it didn't bode good.

"I'm not threatening you. I'm merely explaining how things are going to be around here. The first rule, of course, is that you're to remember you're my exclusive property. The normal way of informing the world is with a wedding ring. In our case we shall have to rely on word of mouth."

"What!" she exclaimed, astonished.

"I will make sure everyone including your father knows how matters are between us. We've already got a good start with your friend Thorne. I expect he'll let your friends know . . ."

"Logan! You can't do that!" she yelped, the coffee cup rattling precariously in her hand. "Affairs are supposed to be *discreet!* One doesn't go around announcing them like a wedding, for heaven's sake! My father would be furious," she added, appalled at the idea of having to explain things to Crawford. He was a man of the world and he would probably understand his daughter involved in a secret romance but he certainly wouldn't condone a publicly announced affair. Crawford had never said anything about Kevin Thorne, even though he must have thought she was having an affair with the artist, but he would have yelled blue murder if she had flaunted it.

"When an affair is discreet, as you call it, people are

left with the impression that one or the other of the partners is still somewhat available. I intend to assure the world that you most definitely are not on the open market any longer."

"Must you talk like that?" she ground out furiously, amber eyes flashing gold sparks as she glared at him.

"Like what?" he asked innocently.

"As if I were a . . . a commodity on which you were trying to corner the market!" she snapped.

"But that's exactly the way I view it," he retorted. "I'm a businessman, as you told me last night."

"Well, I don't have to go along with your terms!" she countered forcefully, angling her chin defiantly.

"Oh, but you do," he smiled loftily. "The alternative is marriage. Take your pick."

"I don't have to have an affair or marry you!"

"Hilary, we both know that I can carry you into that bedroom and within a very short span of time have you agreeing to anything I say. The only reason I'm not using that particular tactic to get you to marry me is because I'm so sick of hearing you carry on about the restaurants. I'm going to prove once and for all that they're not important and this seems to be the only way I can do it. You'll have your proof, sweetheart, but it's going to be on my terms."

Hilary whitened at the sheer determination in his voice. It occurred to her that she was more than a little out of her depth.

"What you're doing is nothing short of blackmail," she breathed.

He lifted one shoulder disinterestedly, watching her through narrowed eyes.

"Logan, please, don't push me so hard. I need time. Everything is happening much too fast and I want time to adjust . . ."

"Does one take time to adjust to the idea of having an affair?" he queried interestedly, one mahogany brow lifting.

"Well, yes, I guess so! I do, at least! I don't normally set up light housekeeping with a man I've only known a few days!" she told him wildly.

Logan drummed the fingers of one hand absently on the arm of his chair while he stared at her thoughtfully. "Let me get this straight. You're now trying to back out of your offer of an affair?"

"No! That is, I . . . ." Hilary subsided in utter confusion. "I need *time!*" she ended on a desperate little wail.

"And if I don't give it to you, you'll accuse me of not loving you sufficiently, right?" Logan supplied brutally.

"Well, you have to admit you're not exactly acting like a man who's deep in love!" she shot back angrily.

"Okay, I'll give you a week before I announce our arrangement to your father and the rest of the world. You can worry about trying to keep Thorne from spreading the news."

Hilary, ready now to seize at any passing straw breathed a thankful little sigh of relief. A week would give her some time to plan. She automatically strove to even the odds a bit more.

"And a week before we . . . we really begin our . . ." she halted, unable to phrase the sentence properly.

"A week before we start sharing the same bed? You drive a hard bargain, don't you, Hilary?"

Hilary, who didn't feel as if she'd driven much of a bargain at all, winced and then looked at him hopefully. "You'll agree to waiting a week?"

"Why not? I suppose I can give in on that point since I have to return to the city tomorrow anyway. I probably won't be able to get back here until Sunday and then I can only stay until Monday. I have a business conference on Tuesday . . ." he paused, apparently going over his schedule mentally. "Yes, beginning Wednesday I should be able to take some time off. I haven't had much vacation this year at all. I can't think of a better way to celebrate a vacation than by starting a new affair, can you?"

One week, Hilary thought dismally. One week to try and straighten out her entire life!

"Now that the timing is settled, shall we go on with the list of rules and regulations?" Logan asked sounding almost cheerful.

"I hardly think that's necessary," Hilary said stiffly.

"On the contrary. I wouldn't want there to be any more misunderstandings of the sort which occurred this morning," he corrected her mildly. "Let's see. In addition to the fact that the affair will be public knowledge and that there are to be absolutely no other men in your life we should probably discuss the matter of finances . . ."

"I've told you, I don't have any intention of being a kept woman!"

"And I believe you, but if I'm going to be spending my weekends here, eating your food and using the facilities, I expect to pay my own way."

"Oh!" she exclaimed, getting to her feet and banging the cup and saucer down furiously on the table. "Why do you have to be so cold-blooded about the whole thing?" she demanded, stalking over to the windows and turning her back on him. Nothing was going right!

"Because you made it clear last night that you didn't want my passion," he answered quietly behind her.

Hilary lowered her head, not knowing how to respond to the accusation. "You don't understand," she whispered brokenly.

"Yes," he said, sounding vaguely surprised. "I think

I do understand. You see, I realized something else after I'd left you last night, Hilary. I realized that you aren't the only one who wants to be married for love."

"What . . . what do you mean?" she asked slowly, swinging around to look at him.

"It's simple. I want what you want: Proof that you love me. Maybe an affair will be a good way to make sure of your feelings for me. In any event it's better than having to listen to you yelling at me on our wedding night that I only married you for the restaurants!"

Hilary flinched at that, but said nothing. Turning back toward the window she finally asked.

"I'll have my proof of your intentions if I can tolerate a flagrant love affair," she stated grimly. "How will you decide whether or not I'm really in love with you? What will constitute your proof?"

"I'll have my proof on the day you beg me to marry you," he said coldly.

Hilary froze, a sudden shaft of fear going through her. "Even if that day arrives, how do you know I'd be begging out of love for you? It might simply mean I've grown unable to deal with a public affair!"

"I'll know because I'm going to turn you down," he said silkily. "And if you decide to continue the affair after that kind of rejection, I'll assume you really are in love. You'd have to be to tolerate that! Not that I'll then decide to go ahead and marry you. To be an effective proof your actions will have to be based on the knowledge that I might not marry you after all, won't they?"

"You're a beast!" she blazed, whirling around to face him. "An arrogant, egotistical beast! What makes you think I'd lower myself to begging you for anything? In fact, what makes you think I'll even let myself be blackmailed like this in the first place?"

"What makes me think you'll do what I want?" he growled softly, getting easily to his feet and moving toward her. "The way you turn to molten gold in my arms, Hilary. That's what makes me think you'll eventually give me exactly what I want. Think carefully before you decide it's the affair you really want now, though, because, as you can see, it carries a lot of strings attached. You'll have to figure out a way to keep your father from raising hell. You'll have to learn how to deal with your friends thinking you're a kept woman, as you call it. After all, you and I will know the financial arrangements are fair, but everyone will assume the opposite. Affairs carry a certain amount of tradition, you realize. And what about the day you recognize that I was telling the truth all along? What will you do when you decide you should have married me while you had the chance? You'll fling yourself into my arms, beg me to marry you, and pray I'm going to say yes. But what if I don't, Hilary?" he challenged, coming closer and closer, making her feel the threat in him. "Perhaps you'll never bring yourself to ask me to marry you because you'll be so afraid of the rejection . . ."

"Stop it!" she begged, feeling tears of frustration and pain in her eyes. She was so terribly confused and he wasn't letting up for a minute. "Let me think, Logan! I've got to have time to think . . ."

"There's nothing left to think about," he countered, taking hold of her arms and forcing her to stand still in front of him. To stand still when all she could think about was running. Running as fast and as far as she could. But he wasn't even allowing her to take that cowardly route. "You've already made your decision, haven't you? You chose the affair . . ."

"No!" she squeaked hoarsely, "You can't make me have an affair with you . . ."

"No?" he repeated and pulled her tightly against him, his mouth descending to devour hers. She felt the full force of his barely leashed anger and desire and crumpled before it. She couldn't fight the passion in him or in herself just then. All she could think about was how awful he had made her notion of an affair sound. Coupled with the knowledge that she couldn't resist him when he chose to take hold of her like this, Hilary knew she was lost.

"All right," she breathed, when he finally freed her lips. "I'll marry you! I'll do what you want, Logan, just give me a little time, I beg you!"

Hilary felt a tremor go through him and told herself it was just her imagination. But she could almost have sworn it was a tremor of sheer, unadulterated relief.

"You'll have a little time," he assured her, setting her back a pace and smiling down into her wide, confused eyes. "You'll have exactly one week, in fact. I told your father this morning we were going to be married next Wednesday." His smile widened with an annoying touch of triumph. "Don't worry, sweetheart. Some day you'll realize that I passed, not failed, the little test you just put me through!"

Chapter Seven

At noontime while caught in the middle of the lunch hour rush at the Silver Salt cellar, the chief thought in Hilary's mind was the one she had been left with after Logan had announced he'd already scheduled their marriage: She'd been outmaneuvered again!

She could hardly believe it. Hilary still wasn't certain exactly how it had happened. The morning had begun in such a chaotic fashion with that disgusting scene between Kevin and Logan in her own living room and then she'd been bounced from the high of thinking that Logan had at last agreed to meet her terms to the low of hearing those terms made to sound horrid. Somewhere during that low point, she'd realized with a groan, he'd sprung the trap. She'd been caught offguard again, weakened and confused and before she knew exactly what was happening, she'd agreed to marry the man.

And the devil had planned it that way all along! He'd told Crawford to expect the marriage on Wednesday before he'd even come to see Hilary that morning! It was humiliating, she told herself, to be so easily maneuvered. No, it was more than that. It was downright awesome!

"Hilary! One of the customers wants the recipe for the cornbread," a waitress yelled, whirling through the kitchen toward the dining room. "What'll I tell him?"

"I'll jot it down," Hilary replied, drying her hands on her apron and reaching for a pad of paper and a pencil. "We should be grateful, you know. One of these days someone will ask for one of our recipes and he'll turn out to be from some fancy food magazine!"

"I can see it now," Ben the cook grinned as he whisked a sauce. "Cornbread Hilary and Herb Dressing Ben. We'll be famous."

"I think I'll title it Cornbread Silver Salt Cellar," Hilary told him firmly. "The restaurant needs the advertising more than you or I. If it makes it big, we'll get taken along for the ride!"

In spite of the multitude of interruptions and tasks, her early morning scene with Logan was never far from Hilary's thoughts. For the rest of the day she agonized over what to do next. Logan hadn't stayed long after winning his victory, certainly not long enough for his victim to recover and begin screaming at him. He'd dropped one of his quick little kisses on her forehead, gazed with laughing eyes into her stunned amber ones and cheerfully reminded her that she was to expect himself and her father for dinner that evening. Then he'd left, leaving her no one to scold or claw. It had all been a perfectly handled boardroom engagement that had left the loser uncertain of anything except the fact that she'd somehow lost a major battle.

A battle or the war? Hilary wondered as she closed up the restaurant and climbed slowly into her little car. She was very much afraid it was the entire war which had been lost that morning. The only event missing was the formal surrender . . .

But she wouldn't give in that easily, she told herself firmly, a feeling of desperation setting in now that there remained only a few hours until she had to face Logan and her father. Of course, she could simply arrange not to be at home, but that would be cowardly. Especially when alternatives still remained. She wasn't exactly weaponless, she reminded herself as she guided the car into the drive of her home. She'd turned the tables on Crawford and his candidates before and one of the most effective tools she'd ever used had been Julia Fane.

Her mind made up, Hilary wasted no time in calling Julia's number and explaining that help was needed once again.

"But, Hilary, I'd love to come to dinner. Your Mr. Saber looked absolutely delightful, and richer than the last one. I'll tell Carl I can't make it tonight and I'll see you for dinner," Julia laughed in anticipation. "I gather your father is not exactly uninteresting, either," she added suggestively.

"Crawford gets around," Hilary agreed drily wondering privately what it would be like to have such an *adventuress* attitude toward men. Julia seemed to live a very exciting sort of life.

"Don't worry, Hilary darling. I'll take care of the charming Logan for you. It will be very much my pleasure!"

Hilary hung up the phone, shaking her head in wonder. Julia amazed her. She knew the blonde would dominate the evening from the moment she arrived. It was always that way when Julia was around. A beautiful, reckless woman who seemed almost larger than life to Hilary. Logan might have been able to resist her when she had stopped for a small chat at the cocktail table the other night, but he'd never been exposed to the full force of Julia Fane on the move. It should be an interesting encounter. And an interesting encounter, Hilary told herself with a touch of professionalism, deserved a carefully planned meal. There wasn't much time but she had a store of recipes that should fit the occasion. She'd swiped a couple of bottles of wine from the Silver Salt Cellar before she'd left that afternoon, so that part was under control. Hilary set to work with her usual efficiency and skill, her task spiced by a strange sense of expectancy.

Julia, as agreed, arrived first that evening, sweeping through the door in a daringly-cut frock of some clinging material in a mind-jolting, electric blue. She looked saucy and sexy and self-assured, Hilary thought with the first touch of dismay. Perhaps this hadn't been such a good idea, after all. But that was ridiculous. Julia, to be effective, had to look this good and that was the whole point, wasn't it?

Dressed in a simply styled beige dress with only a bright, striped belt for color, Hilary suddenly felt underdressed. Julia fairly gleamed with expensive, glittering jewelry and the brilliant blue of the dress set off her deceptively casual blonde hair to perfection. Assuming, of course, that any man would be able to drag his gaze away from the low-cut front of the gown long enough to admire the rest of her!

"I'm looking forward to this evening, Hilary," Julia announced cheerfully, as she accepted a drink and arranged herself on the couch. "I had quite a good time with the last one. That was number three, wasn't it? Yes, we enjoyed ourselves, but he became rather tiresome. You know how it is," she finished with a delicate shrug of one nearly nude shoulder.

Hilary, who knew she didn't know how it was at all,

nodded quickly and than rose again at the sound of the doorbell. This was it, she thought nervously, disgusted with the unexpected dampness of her palms. Logan would probably recognize instantly what she was up to, but would he be able to resist? With a sudden pang, Hilary found a small part of her hoping he could resist. But that was silly. What would it prove? Only that the restaurants were more important to him than the lures of Julia Fane!

"Hello, Crawford," Hilary said politely, lifting her face for her father's kiss of greeting. The action gave her an excuse to avoid meeting the gleaming gray-green eyes of the tall man standing on the next step.

"Hilary, my dear," Crawford exclaimed, obviously delighted. "I couldn't be more pleased! I knew Logan was the right one. Knew it the minute I met him. And tonight we get to celebrate the engagement, I understand? Logan tells me the wedding is set for next Wednesday?"

"We can talk about it later," Hilary demurred. "Won't you come in? I've invited someone else to make up the numbers." She raised her eyes to meet Logan's and found it took an effort of will not to lower them again. He was gazing down at her with so much warmth and possessiveness . . .

"Good evening, Hilary," he said quietly, stepping forward as Crawford moved on into the hall. Deliberately he placed a palm on each side of her face and kissed her soundly on the mouth. "I'm glad to see you're here where you're supposed to be this evening!"

"You had some reason to think I might be gone?" she retaliated in a low hiss.

"It occurred to me you might panic and do something foolish," he admitted with a low chuckle, his gaze moving hungrily over her. "You're looking cool and charming this evening, little one. A delight, as usual."

Hilary felt the heat moving into her cheeks and stepped away. "Please come in, Logan. There's someone I want you to meet. . . ."

But there was no need to make formal introductions. The sound of voices from the living room made it clear that Crawford had already discovered the other guest. Hilary could hear the suave, sophisticated tones of her father in action and sighed. She had certainly served up a gourmet meal for Julia Fane tonight. Two eminently attractive, very masculine men reeking of money and success. Both males were dressed in jackets and slacks that had clearly been hand-tailored and both wore the clothes and the success with authority.

Logan strode into the living room, Hilary trailing slightly, apprehensively, behind him and stopped short. Julia was just retrieving her hand from Crawford's with a laughing, teasing comment. Crawford was all easy flattery and smooth smile.

Logan flicked an amused glance down at Hilary and said very softly, "I see there are going to be a few last-ditch campaigns after all. You surprise me, sweetheart. I would have thought you were smart enough to know when to surrender." Before she could retaliate, he moved forward to greet Julia with casual polish.

"Hello, Julia, it's nice to see you again," he said politely, accepting the graceful hand being extended.

"I've been looking forward to it," she assured him in her sultry tones.

"You two know each other?" Crawford inquired mildly.

"Hilary introduced us the other evening, didn't you, sweetheart?" he said smiling at Hilary.

"I see," Crawford said reflectively. He'd never met the woman responsible for compromising candidate number three but he knew his daughter and he was no fool. He was quite capable of putting two and two together, Hilary realized as her father's eyes met hers consideringly.

"If you'll excuse me," she said quickly, "I'll go and get some drinks . . ."

"I'll help you," Logan said before she could scurry off to the kitchen. "What will you have, Julia?"

"Whatever you're having will be fine," Julia purred with a deliberate sweep of her long lashes.

"And you, Crawford?" Logan went on, ignoring the lashes.

"A martini, I think, Logan."

"Fine," Logan nodded, following close on Hilary's heels as she slipped away in the direction of the kitchen. There he caught up with her, of course. There wasn't any room to hide in such a small environment, she realized sadly. But he didn't seem unduly annoyed she decided, watching a bit anxiously as he strolled in behind her, going immediately to the liquor cabinet.

"You are turning out to be a most obstructionistic sort of princess," he told her blandly, fixing two martinis instead of one. Hilary wondered if he'd forgotten that Julia had ordered whatever he was having. "Not content with letting me think there was another man in the picture, you're now going to throw me into the arena with that she-wolf. How could you do such a thing to an innocent man, Hilary?"

"Didn't you realize that all princesses put any knight who comes courting through his paces?" she retaliated, not attempting to pretend that she didn't know what he was talking about. "Besides, I don't see it as throwing a man into the arena. I see it more as a contest between a full-sized lion and a she-wolf!"

"Flattery will get you nowhere, my sweet," he grinned, reaching for his bottle of scotch. "I'll take up your challenge, naturally, but there'll be a reckoning afterward!"

Hilary flicked a wary glance at him as she heaped a platter with an assortment of dainty appetizers. "That's hardly fair, is it?" she countered with a patently false airiness. "I mean, in all the stories I ever read the knight never gets even with the princess for all he had to go through in order to prove himself!"

"They all end with the couple living happily ever after, don't they?" he demanded, pouring a sherry into the fourth glass.

"Well, yes . . ."

"Then somewhere along the line the knight must have taken the princess down a peg or two. How else could things end happily for both of them?"

"Chauvinist!" she snapped, sweeping out of the kitchen with her tray and leaving him to follow. The low chuckle behind her was most annoying.

"Here you are, Julia," Logan announced a moment later, handing the blonde a martini. "I decided to exercise a bartender's discretion and fixed this for you, instead. You look more like a martini drinker to me than a scotch drinker. What do you think, Crawford?" he added, handing the older man the other glass.

"Definitely," Crawford agreed, watching as Logan handed the sherry to his daughter. "All martini drinkers are the adventuresome sort and Julia, here, is quite adventuresome. Did you know she's a sailing enthusiast, Logan?"

"No, I didn't," Logan returned blandly. "You must get Crawford to take you out on his boat, Julia. It's quite a beauty."

"Do you sail?" Julia asked him sweetly, obviously expecting a positive answer.

"No, I'm afraid not. I have very little interest in the sport, as a matter of fact. And then there's the cost of the boat to consider. Crawford can afford to pour his money into the water like that, but I can't," he told her deliberately.

"Really?" Julia inquired appraisingly, slanting a sidelong glance at Hilary who shook her head in a small negative gesture. Julia musn't get the idea Logan wasn't wealthy. "I had understood you were more than successful in your own right. Hilary said you are president of your own company in Los Angeles . . ."

"Oh, I've done well enough, I suppose, but Crawford could buy and sell me several times over, couldn't you, Crawford?" Logan said chattily, helping himself to one of Hilary's appetizers.

"Well, perhaps not *several* times," Crawford smiled kindly, "But I have had a few more years to build up my holdings. Then, too, Logan's at a point in his career where all the money should be poured back into the business. I'm at a stage where I can sit back and enjoy mine."

Hilary felt a wave of definite unease sweep over her. What was going on here? She moved quickly to set the record straight. The look in Julia's beautiful eyes had a distinctly mercenary touch.

"They're both just being modest, Julia," she said with an effort at a casual laugh. "Logan's firm is very successful, I assure you. Here, have another snack. The only reason he doesn't own a sailboat is because he has other interests."

"Oh?" Julia tried again. "Do you ski, Logan?

"I'm afraid not," he told her ruefully. "Much too busy most of the time to get away. Crawford is quite an athlete, though. Didn't you say something about a condominium in Aspen just the other day?" he inquired politely, shifting the conversation back to Hilary's father.

"Yes. I was thinking of selling it since I'm doing so

much of my skiing in Europe these days, but I expect I'll hold onto it through another season."

"What are your major interests, Logan?" Julia said gamely.

"Salt cellars," he stated succinctly and Hilary choked on her sherry. "I've got quite a collection, I'm proud to say," he went on cheerfully, slapping his bride-to-be on the back with a hearty action. "Sometimes I think that's the main reason Hilary agreed to marry me. She wants to acquire my collection and what better way than through marriage? Do you know anything about salt cellars, Julia?"

"Well, no, not really," Julia admitted hesitantly, looking rather blank.

"Fascinating hobby. Just the other day I was lucky enough to come across the nicest little cloisonné piece. Did Hilary tell you about it?"

"No, she . . ." Julia tried desperately to stem the tide, but it was hopeless. Logan had the bit between his teeth and there was no stopping him. For the next twenty minutes Hilary listened in mounting horror as her knight routed his latest opponent by the simple tactic of boring her to tears. Poor Julia turned with evident relief to Crawford when the first conversational opening appeared and Hilary, knowing defeat when she saw it, rose to announce that dinner was served.

"Don't you think Logan and my Hilary are ideally suited?" Crawford inquired of Julia as he led her toward the table. "It's so nice when two people share the same interests. Personally, I'd never be able to tolerate the hours of antique shop browsing that goes into finding one salt cellar, would you?"

"No," Julia agreed with a beautiful smile aimed solely at Crawford. "I prefer more active pursuits. You were right when you said I was more the, er, adventuresome type."

"Not like Hilary and Logan," Crawford chuckled, glancing affectionately at the other pair. "Good, solid, business types. Like I said, as soon as I met Logan I knew he'd be the right one for my girl. She needs someone restrained and placid. It's a myth, you know, that opposites should go together. Hilary will be very happy with someone who understands her because he's a lot like her." Crawford beamed benignly on the other two as he pronounced his opinion while seating Julia.

Unavoidably, Hilary met Logan's eyes as Crawford described their restrained and placid relationship. There was so much laughter in the gray-green gaze that she couldn't help a wry response. In spite of herself a smile curved the corner of her mouth as she privately acknowledged that her father either had no inkling of the stormy state of affairs between herself and candidate number four or was deliberately misleading Julia. Whatever the reason behind his actions, he had unwittingly generated a bond between Hilary and Logan as they sat opposite each other at the table. There was a certain undeniable pleasure to be derived from knowing that the outside world had no conception of the level of passion two restrained and placid businesspeople could reach. It was something private and vastly amusing. And for a moment she shared the small joke with Logan.

"How did you know Logan was such a pattern of restrained behavior, Crawford?" Hilary demanded, serving the unusual buttermilk and vegetable soup from the large tureen in the center of the table.

"I'd seen him in action in various meetings and a few social gettogethers," Crawford explained cheerfully. "Always calm, cool and collected. Can't imagine him losing his temper or being too demanding. At the same time he's got a good head on his shoulders and he's not a weakling. He'll be much better for you than the others . . ." Crawford broke off belatedly realizing that he'd said too much.

"The others, Crawford?" Hilary smiled innocently, ignoring Logan's nonverbal message to keep quiet. "What others?"

"The, uh, other men you've met recently," Crawford explained earnestly, showing great interest in his soup. "A new recipe that you're experimenting with, Hilary?" he inquired lightly.

"Most of the other men I've met recently have been introduced to me by you, Crawford," Hilary smiled politely, passing the rolls that were to accompany the soup.

"Business associates," Crawford said loftily. "Have a roll, Julia?"

"You certainly have produced a number of 'business associates' lately," Hilary went on in a mockingly blithe tone. "Perhaps I'm acting hastily in agreeing to marry Logan. It might be wiser to see whom you next invite down to Santa Barbara . . . ouch!"

"What's wrong, Hilary?" Julia asked quickly.

"Logan just squashed five of my toes," Hilary muttered, glaring at her intended.

"I'm sorry, honey. Such a small table and I have such large feet! I'll try to be more careful where I place them," Logan said in a smooth way which did nothing to hide the warning in his words. At least, Hilary decided wrathfully, the warning was quite obvious to herself. Julia and Crawford seemed oblivious. "It won't happen again," he smiled and left unspoken the rest of his words which, Hilary knew, could be roughly interpreted as "unless you don't keep quiet on the subject of the other candidates."

"Hilary's got a fine sense of humor," Logan went on, speaking to Julia and Crawford. "It's one of the first things I noticed about her. Did I ever tell you exactly how we met, Crawford? She just showed up in my office one day, announcing herself as my . . ."

"Excuse me, darling," Hilary interrupted in wifely tones. "Would you mind helping me clear the table? I see we're all about finished with the soup and I'm going to need a little help with the lamb." She rose pointedly, leaving him with no option but to do the same. He collected plates willingly enough and followed her dutifully into the kitchen where she whirled to confront him the moment he came through the door.

"Don't you dare repeat that story of how I got in to see you by telling your secretary I was your future wife!" she snapped in a barely suppressed snarl.

Logan, his hands laden with plates, smiled down at her frowning features. "I'll make a deal with you, sweetheart. You say nothing about the other candidates and I'll refrain from telling the story of our first meeting."

"Why shouldn't I say anything about the others? Everyone already knows about them, anyway?" she challenged.

"You won't say anything because it will embarrass your father and it will make me very angry. Is that reason enough?" One mahogany brow lifted inquiringly.

For an instant Hilary studied him, one foot tapping impatiently on the tiled floor then, without a word she turned, hoisted the lamb platter and thrust it toward him.

"Here," she mocked, "Show the folks what a nice, restrained, undemanding, helpful sort of husband you're going to be!"

Logan set down the plates he was holding and accepted the tray. "Anything to preserve the Boy Scout image," he nodded agreeably and then flashed her a quick grin before starting out of the kitchen. "Just remember that when I'm around you the facade is always in danger of slipping. I've been provoked enough for one evening. Much more prodding on your part and I won't wait until Crawford and Julia have gone before I extract what I feel is owing."

Julia Fane made a few half-hearted attempts to fulfill her promise to Hilary but it was clear her heart was no longer in the project of seducing Logan Saber. Over the lamb she tried to strike up a conversation with him on the subject of the modern approach to romance.

"You mean a string of affairs?" he clarified baldly. "That's all very fine for a while but I'm basically a homebody. Hearth, home and Hilary, that's the life for me," he added, sending a patronizingly affectionate smile at Hilary who felt like dumping the contents of her water glass over his head. And then, as he did whenever Julia tried for an opening with him, he bounced her neatly back into Crawford's lap.

Crawford made it clear he was waiting to catch her with open arms. It really came as no surprise to anyone when the older man invited Julia to go dancing with him after dinner. The blonde accepted willingly enough as she forked up the last of her walnut lemon tart. She threw Hilary one last apologetic glance and then, with an "I tried" shrug, turned back to the rewarding task of conversing with Crawford.

"A fine meal, as always," her father told Hilary later as he stood at the door, Julia on his arm, preparing to leave. "Logan, you'll be marrying yourself a terrific cook. Well, we'll be off, I believe. Ready, Julia?"

"I'm always ready, Crawford," Julia smiled provocatively. "Shall we take my car or yours?"

"Let's take yours. Logan can use mine to get back to the cottage. Besides, I've been wanting to try out the new Porsche. That is yours parked in the drive, isn't it?"

134

"Oh, yes, it's mine."

Logan hovered beside Hilary as the four said their good nights, making her feel like a much-married wife bidding good evening to guests who'd come for dinner. All that was lacking, she thought irritatedly, was the ring on her finger and the knowledge that she would be climbing sleepily into bed with Logan after the dishes had been done.

"Well, I'd call that a reasonably successful evening, wouldn't you?" Logan asked with satisfaction as the door closed. Hilary watched nervously as he loosened his tie in a move that brought back memories of the previous evening. She stepped hurriedly around him, heading for the security of the kitchen.

"Not particularly," she retorted spiritedly making a great deal of noise as she stacked dishes into the dishwasher with a vengeance. She pretended to ignore his large form as he came to lean in the doorway, watching her with eyes that gleamed in amusement. Amusement and something else.

"Ah, Hilary," he chided gently. "Aren't you going to be a cheerful loser? Or do I have to make you admit you're secretly glad Julia left with Crawford instead of me."

Hilary gave a small exclamation of outrage, recognizing that he was right. She had experienced a definite lightening of the spirit when she'd come to the realization that Logan had passed the reckless blonde test. Still, she clung gamely to the offensive.

"It proves nothing, except possibly that the restaurants are more important to you than a fling with Julia Fane!" She avoided his eyes, busying herself industriously with the work at hand.

Behind her he heaved a sigh of exasperation. "Enough games for this evening, Hilary," he told her, a distinct edge to his voice. "I have to go back to the city tomorrow. Leave the dishes alone and come and show me how much you'll miss me when I go back to L.A. tomorrow ."

Startled, she glanced up at him and straightened slowly at the expression in his eyes.

"Now, Logan . . ." she began carefully, not liking the way he was studying her.

"Come here, Hilary," he ordered softly, an underlying note of passion beginning to surface in his manner. A note she couldn't safely ignore.

"Logan," she said slowly, "I'm sorry about tonight . . ."

"No you're not," he corrected at once. "But I do want to hear you say you're glad I passed the test." He didn't move but somehow he seemed to be filling her kitchen with very large and very dangerous maleness.

"Hadn't you better be getting back to the cottage? If you have to be at work in the morning . . ." She felt the tension growing in her.

"Hilary," he growled, "Stop talking and come here. I deserve some reward for my little victory tonight, don't you think?"

"No, I don't . . ." she began heatedly, already conscious of the excitement his look was generating. Why could this man affect her so easily? It wasn't at all fair! Logan shifted ever so slightly in the doorway and Hilary jumped. He was quite serious, she realized. It would be safest not to defy him. Cautiously she edged forward.

"What exactly do you want?" she demanded, trying to inject her words with disinterested hauteur.

"A kiss for starters," he said consideringly. "In all the fairytales the hero always winds up with the lady in his arms."

"That's after he's completed all the challenges!"

"There's more to come?" Logan smiled dangerously.

"In that case I'll just take a little on account. *Come here, Hilary!*" The last three words came out in a totally different tone, surprising her with its whiplash of command. He'd never used that level of intimidation with her before and she acknowledged ruefully that it was effective. Hilary found herself responding without further thought.

"The most annoying, obstinate little thing," Logan whispered as she approached him warily. "Why so cautious, Hilary? You know you love it once you're in my arms. . . ." When she stood only a pace away from him he reached out a hand and snagged her around the waist, tugging her the rest of the way toward him.

"Now," he said with drawling assurance, "I'm going to kiss you until you tell me how glad you are that I'm here and not out dancing with Julia Fane."

Wordlessly, Hilary stood in the warm circle of his embrace as he bent his head to take her lips. He was right, she thought fleetingly as the familiar magic took hold. Logan Saber had power over her. But how much power did she have over him? Was hers only as strong as the lure of the restaurants?

But when his mouth covered hers it was impossible to think logically. There was only a need to respond, to satisfy, to please. And it grew stronger every time he took her in his arms. Tonight she had half expected to see the last of the man. It had seemed so likely that he would leave her life with Julia Fane on his arm but instead he was here with her. Right now that seemed to be all that was really important. Hilary's arms circled his neck and with a sigh she melted against Logan's hard frame. Life was short and the opportunity to know this kind of feeling came seldom to a woman like herself . . .

"Hilary my sweet, why do you doubt me?" Logan

grated against her skin, responding to her surrender with a passion that threatened to dominate both of them. "Tell me," he urged. "Tell me how much you'll miss me . . ."

"I'll miss you, Logan," she managed, curling her head into his shoulder as his hands swept the length of her body in long, possessive strokes that made her tremble. "I don't know how or why I let you do this to me but I can't seem to help myself!"

"Have you considered that you're probably in love with me?" he whispered half teasingly, his lips on the softness of her throat. "In the end, you're going to tell me that, too," he promised. "I've made you say that you want me, that you'll miss me. One of these days you'll admit that you love me. . . ."

Hilary said nothing, feeling her tongue unable to shape the words of denial. At least he wasn't going to push her that far tonight. . . . When his hands moved to her shoulders, setting her gently away from him she blinked in heavy-lidded surprise. He smiled down at her, amusement and passion combining in the hard lines of his face.

"First I have to give you something," he said softly, reaching into the pocket of his coat and withdrawing a small case. "After that we can go back to what we've got started . . ." He ripped off the wrapping paper and opened the box.

"What is it?" Hilary asked, trying to shake off the langour of the moment. "Another salt cellar?"

"No." The corner of his mouth quirked slightly. "Give me your arm," he added reaching for her wrist.

Frowning a bit in confusion, Hilary allowed him to take hold of her. A ring, she thought suddenly, he was going to put a ring on her finger. She wasn't sure she wanted that. Not yet. A ring was a mark of ownership, a sign of possession and Logan was a possessive man.

Even if he didn't love her he had vowed to own her. As his wife she would be expected to respect his possessiveness. No, it was too soon . . .

But it wasn't a ring. Logan withdrew a gold circlet from the box and clasped it firmly around her wrist with a distinctly final sounding snap. He released her hand and watched her face as she examined the gift.

"It's . . . it's very unusual," Hilary said slowly, at once drawn to the rather barbaric simplicity of the beaten gold band. There was something about it that reminded her of another world, another era. Something symbolic and a little dangerous. Then she had it.

"It looks like an ancient manacle," she said with a trace of unease.

"Do you like it?" he asked, watching her intently, the gray-green eyes demanding an answer.

"It's stunning," she said honestly. "Very different." She twisted the strange bracelet, eyeing the catch. "How does the clasp work?" she inquired curiously. She couldn't accept it, of course.

"It doesn't," he told her with deliberate menace.

"What do you mean?" she demanded, the sense of unease turning into a feeling of being trapped.

"I paid the jeweler a fortune this afternoon to modify it so that, once closed, the bracelet can't be opened again."

"You did what?" she squeaked, astounded.

"I didn't want something you could take on and off at your own pleasure," he told her, his eyes never leaving her stricken face. "I wanted a piece of jewelry that was a constant reminder of whose woman you are . . ."

"A slave bracelet!" she gasped in rising fury. "Not very subtle, are you, Logan? What makes you think I won't go out tomorrow and have this thing cut off?" She glared at him, her hand itching to strike his face. If only he weren't so much larger . . .

139

"You do and I'll turn you over my knee the moment I find out. And since I'm most likely to find out next Sunday when I go to the Silver Salt Cellar for brunch, it should provide quite a spectacle for your customers!"

"See here, Logan, I won't be treated like this!" Throwing all caution to the winds, Hilary swung the manacled hand in an arc that connected with the side of his face in a stinging slap. And then prudence took hold and she turned, running for the bedroom.

He followed. She could feel him gaining easily on her but there was time; barely enough time. With a last burst of speed, Hilary bolted through the door and flung it shut behind her, snapping the lock into place immediately. With a sigh of relief, she sagged against the wood paneling and wondered what he would do now.

The gleam of gold from the bracelet flashed richly in the light of the bedside lamp.

It wasn't until she heard his car leaving that Hilary finally realized Logan wasn't going to break down her door and sweep her into his arms. Maybe, just maybe, she decided feeling unaccountably depressed, she'd gone too far.

Chapter Eight

The fragrance of flowers woke Hilary from a restless sleep the following morning. A lush, rich, fragrance, she thought without opening her eyes. Perhaps the neighbor's roses had come into bloom early. Half-consciously she turned her head in the direction of the scent, her mind beginning to spin already with thoughts of Logan. Had he given up on her entirely last night? Decided the restaurants weren't worth the hectic courtship? She found the thought so disturbing that dampness appeared behind her closed lids, moistening the lashes. No! She would not cry!

Why was she so sad? Hadn't she known all along how he really felt? He had simply used her weak point against her in the same manner that she had used the weaknesses of the previous candidates against them. Face it, she told herself forcefully, you ran into a stronger opponent. Someone who knew exactly how to get through your defenses by appealing to the streak of wild romanticism which no one else had ever even suspected existed. A clever businessman who had known that she secretly craved both a friend and a lover and had provided both. . . .

The fragrance of the roses seemed stronger than ever. Hilary sniffed gently, not certain whether the action was an effort to swallow the incipient tears or an attempt to inhale more of the roses. Funny, she hadn't realized the neighbors even grew roses. Perhaps it was some other blossom's aroma. She shifted her nose slightly and opened her eyes with a sleepy effort.

The first thing she saw was the luscious, velvety red rose lying two inches away on her pillow.

Her sleepy mind was still trying to absorb the implications of the first flower when she realized there was another beyond it. And another. . . . Disbelievingly Hilary moved the gold manacled hand to touch the petals of the nearest rose. How in the world could they be real? She must be dreaming!

"Oh!" She withdrew her hand quickly as she encountered a small spike on the stem.

"They're like you, Hilary," Logan's voice said in gravelly, affectionate amusement from somewhere near the foot of her bed. "Highly desirable but well-protected by thorns."

"Logan!" she exclaimed, totally startled. "What are you doing here? How did you get in?" she added, her eyes flying to where her bedroom door stood open. She had left it locked last night when she'd finally gone to bed. Her mind whirled in astonishment and a strange gladness. He hadn't left her in disgust! She turned her wide-eyed gaze back to where he lounged in the red padded chair which matched the gold and red bedspread. She ought to be far more surprised to see him than she was . . .

"I picked the lock on your door," he explained blandly. "It only takes about one minute. Remember that the next time you seek refuge in the bedroom."

He could just as easily have followed her into the room last night, Hilary realized. She'd half expected him to do that and so he'd deliberately done something else, instead. She shook her head in rueful comprehension, propping herself up on her elbow to stare at him. A flower moved as she elevated herself and she saw that red roses had been cascaded over her entire bed.

"You've done it again, haven't you?" she demanded with a wry twist of her lips. "You realize I thought you'd probably break down my door last night?"

"Any other night I might have done exactly that. But I knew you'd been upset by the bracelet." He flicked a quick, satisfied glance at the band of gold on her wrist. "So I decided to give you a little time to get over the shock. You had been expecting a ring, hadn't you?"

"One of these days, Logan," she whispered, "I'll learn that it's better not to try and predict your actions." She looked around at the beautiful flowers and then met his eyes again, determined to say what she'd awakened in the middle of the night wishing she'd said before he'd left her.

"I'm sorry I slapped you."

"Are you?" he asked enigmatically. "Why?"

"Until I'd met you," she sighed, "I'd never struck a man in my life. Of course, I'd never been so provoked before, either! But all in all I don't think it's a very fair tactic for a woman to use against a man."

"Because if he responds in kind he's automatically a brute?"

She nodded mutely, a long braid shifting to fall over her shoulder. She wasn't certain exactly why she was apologizing. He'd deserved the blow!

"You don't have to have any qualms with me, sweetheart," Logan grinned in sudden, devastating humor. "I won't hesitate in the least to get myself labeled a brute if that's what it takes. I didn't retaliate last night for the simple reason that I figured I had it coming!"

"You did!" she declared instantly, sitting farther up in bed and clutching the sheet tightly. She threw out her wrist in exasperation. "This thing is absolutely pagan! It's barbaric and you know it! I ought to look up a jeweler first thing this morning and get it removed!" Now that she knew he hadn't changed his mind about the marriage, Hilary felt free to tell him exactly how she felt.

"It's pagan and barbaric," Logan began deliberately, getting to his feet and coming across the room to tower over her, "Because what we have between us is a little pagan and barbaric." The gray-green eyes gleamed down at her and he removed a rose to clear a space for himself on the quilt. An instant later he sat down, his arms extended to either side of her body, trapping her against the bedclothes. "And you won't dare have it removed, will you, sweetheart?"

She felt the fierce warmth of his hard, solid body, saw the determination in his eyes and, although he hadn't actually touched her, knew the strength in his hands. Talk about pagan and barbaric! Unconsciously, the tip of Hilary's tongue touched the edge of her lip as she tried to resist deeply hidden feminine instincts. Instincts which said that the way to pacify the lion was to please him. Change the growl to a purr by using her own woman-magic against the intimidating maleness of him.

The urge to try the ancient female tactics grew irresistible as she lay trapped on her rose-strewn bed and almost against her own will she touched the fingers of her gold-bound wrist to the side of his face, stroking his cheek in a delicate motion which made his eyes narrow in poorly concealed surprise.

"No, Logan," she said softly, lowering her lashes to

veil her own amber gaze in mystery. "I won't have it removed. Not if you really care . . ." She smiled invitingly, feeling a rush of delightful power as the gleam in Logan's eyes took on the sheen of desire. Oh! What was wrong with her? She had no business playing games like this with a man who could bring her to her knees when he chose to exert his own brand of magic. It was a dangerous, incredibly stupid thing to do and, Hilary told herself, if it weren't for the fact that she had awakened to a totally unreal scene in her own bedroom, she would never have risked it. But the real world seemed far away . . .

"I care, Hilary," Logan growled, lowering his head to kiss her. "Oh, how I want you!" His mouth closed over hers and she let her lips soften and part. Instantly he took advantage of the chance to invade the warmth and moistness of her.

"Logan," she sighed when she could, running the palms of her hands down his shirt-covered back. "I didn't think you'd come back . . ."

"You could never keep me away," he vowed huskily, pulling back the sheet which interfered with his exploring hands. "Haven't you learned that yet? So stubborn. So sweet in my arms and so stubborn!" His mouth moved back to hers when she tried to speak, taking her lips once more with all the unsubtleness of a conqueror. A conqueror who has discovered that his need puts him at the mercy of the conquered.

And Hilary found her taste of power utterly exhilarating. As Logan had observed once before, the question of who was seducing whom was highly debatable. But regardless of the answers to that question, it was Logan who pulled back, albeit reluctantly.

"I have to go, sweetheart," he whispered heavily, his hand cupping her breast as he broke the embrace. "My plane leaves shortly and I don't want our first time together to be hurried. When I come back on Sunday we can take our time . . ." He leaned forward again, dropping a quick, hard kiss on her love-softened mouth and with an apparent effort of will pulled himself off the bed. His eyes swept over her, drinking in the sight of her lying among the roses and a fiercely possessive smile shaped his mouth.

"When I come back on Sunday," he repeated with satisfaction and sheer male anticipation, "There will be ample time to hear you say the words I want to hear. Goodbye, Hilary." He dragged his gaze away, walking quickly over to the red chair and retrieving his coat. He paused once more at the door, turning to look at her. "Behave yourself, honey. Remember that you're mine."

"Or what?" she smiled beguilingly.

"Do you *really* want to know?" he countered, and then he was gone, leaving her in a lonely bed amid a wreath of roses.

The essence of unreality which had greeted her that morning clung to Hilary all day long. It was only because of long standing habits and concentration that she was able to maintain a reasonably normal facade in front of the staff and clientele of the Silver Salt Cellar. When her father and Julia dropped in for lunch and to announce that they were going sailing Hilary managed a normal conversation, smiled at Julia to show there was no hard feelings and ignored her father's knowing look. Let him take the credit, she told herself cheerfully. She would never have met Logan Saber if it wasn't for Crawford's interference.

"What an unusual bracelet," Julia remarked as she prepared to leave on Crawford's arm. "Is it new?" She smiled at Hilary, her elegant boating togs revealing a great deal of leg and chest.

"Logan gave it to me," Hilary said calmly, pausing at

the door of the Silver Salt Cellar to wish them farewell. "It's kind of an engagement present," she added carefully, seeing no need to explain that it was more of a chain than a gift.

"Then things worked out for the best last night after all, didn't they?" Julia grinned happily.

"Come along, Julia, I want to get out on the water while we still have some decent wind. See you later, Hilary," Crawford said with mild impatience. He leaned down and kissed his daughter lightly on the cheek. "Take care, dear. I know you're probably missing Logan but he'll be back on Sunday, won't he?"

"Yes."

"Good. I told him he was welcome to stay at the cottage again but he said he'd rather put up at a local motel. Can't say that I blame him. My comings and goings probably kept him awake most of the night! 'Bye, dear!"

Hilary watched them leave with a small shake of her head. What a couple. She loved her father and she liked Julia but in a sense they were both a little alien to her. Well, each to his own. Why was it that Logan who often struck her as being from another, more primitive point in time seemed not the least bit alien? Annoying, exciting, intimidating, charming, perhaps, but not alien. In fact, there were moments when she knew beyond a doubt that he was the only man on earth who really understood her. The thought of a man holding that much power over her was unsettling. There was a small frown on her face when she turned away from the door and started back through the dining room.

By eight o'clock that night Hilary resigned herself to the fact that Logan probably wasn't going to call. She had been so convinced he would! Surely a man who invaded his future bride's bedroom at dawn to pour roses over her would call that evening? Was this another aspect of his tactics? Was he deliberately not calling because he knew she would be expecting it? Oh, that man! He was getting far too adroit at keeping her off balance. She was going to have to regain some control!

At nine o'clock Hilary put down the book on accounting for small businesses and glared at the silent telephone. Perhaps he was tired. He'd said he had a lot of work to do. He might simply have put in a full day at the office and had gone home to fall sound asleep. He might have had the best intentions in the world but had been unable to carry them out. Of course, she told herself, there was nothing to prevent her from calling him. How would he react to that?

She knew exactly how he would react! He would be delighted that she was so far under his spell as to be the one to call first. Did she want to give him that much satisfaction? He was already so sure of her. She didn't even have his home number, she reminded herself, sitting back in the chair and picking up the book again. Five minutes later she picked up the phone and asked for information. His number was probably unlisted anyway.

But it wasn't. At nine-fifteen she sat by the phone, Logan's number on a piece of paper clutched in her hand. What excuse could she use for calling? To thank him for the roses? That was ridiculous. To ask him to pick up a new salt cellar for her? That sounded pretty thin. How about to find out what time she should expect him on Sunday? No, he'd already told her he'd be in town in time for brunch at the Silver Salt Cellar.

Feeling like a fool, Hilary dialed very slowly and very carefully, almost praying that no one would answer.

But someone did answer and it wasn't Logan.

"Hello?" The voice was low, pleasant and very female.

"Hello," Hilary got out finally, feeling as if the world were dissolving around her. A woman! She hadn't counted on that possibility. No wonder Logan hadn't called! He had a woman there! "I . . . I was calling for Logan," she forced herself to say with a semblance of normality.

"He's not here at the moment. I'll have him call, if you like. Do you want to leave your name and number?"

"No, I . . . who's this?" Appalled, Hilary listened to herself ask the question. Why didn't she simply hang up? What more did she need to know?

"This is Maryann," Maryann said as if anyone who knew Logan must know her. Were they that close? Was that why the lovely Julia hadn't succeeded in luring Logan away from Hilary and the restaurants? That man! How dare he? Hilary felt the anger boiling up inside until it became almost unmanageable. With an effort of will she hung onto the phone, saying that she did not wish to leave a message. Then with unnatural gentleness she broke the connection. But instead of replacing the receiver, she left it off the hook. Then, in a dismal fog compounded of a heretofore unknown anger and unhappiness, she went to bed.

Hilary didn't replace the phone until she left for the restaurant early Friday morning. At the Silver Salt Cellar she threw herself into the day's routine. This was one of the days when the Cellar stayed opened for dinner and there were additional preparations needed for the evening. In keeping with the normal pattern the restaurant would feature entrees based on what was fresh and appealing to the cook and to Hilary. The menu varied every weekend. Tonight Ben had decided on an avocado mousse with crabmeat along with other interesting items such as a tomato pesto tart, an elegant shrimp dish and a luscious custard called Burnt Cream.

For the first time Hilary found herself having to force her enthusiasm for Ben's creations. She knew she shouldn't let the voice on Logan's phone upset her so much but there seemed to be no help for it. She wanted to claw and scream and berate like a fishwife and she had absolutely no right . . .

Of course she had rights she thought grimly glancing down at the manacle on her wrist. If Logan expected her to be bound only to him, she had every right to demand the same in return! But what if he didn't choose to honor her demands? What if he told her, in effect, to turn a blind eye on his private life? She couldn't do it, Hilary realized. No matter how much she might want him, she couldn't tolerate sharing him with another woman. If the restaurants meant enough to him, perhaps he would kick the lovely Maryann out of his home. But would she be followed by a string of other Maryanns? How could Hilary possibly keep tabs on a husband who was going to spend part of his time in Los Angeles. In fact, how could a marriage survive when the couples lived apart during the week? Or was Logan expecting her to give up the restaurant? It was all so complicated and there was so little time left. Perhaps this was exactly the sort of marriage Logan wanted, Hilary thought as she scrubbed vegetables. The woman who usually prepared the vegetables had phoned in sick. It was going to be a busy evening.

It was early in the afternoon when Hilary was called to the Cellar's phone. She took the receiver with hands still wet from handling the vegetables and said a brisk hello.

"Hilary? This is Logan."

Hilary nearly dropped the phone. For some reason his call at the restaurant hadn't been expected. The Silver Salt Cellar represented the business side of Hilary's life. Emotional confrontations with Logan

Saber were supposed to take place outside of her normal world.

"Hello," she said stiffly and then, totally unable to help herself, she added flatly, "Who's Maryann?"

"My sister," he responded instantly, sounding rather grim.

"Oh!"

"Is that all you can say after leaving your phone off the hook for the entire night?" he demanded wrathfully.

"Well, how was I to know who she was?" Hilary retorted, feeling vastly relieved and needing to get the emotions which had been festering inside out into the open. "You might have told me your sister lived with you! Or did you deliberately say nothing, hoping I would call and get jealous? That's probably it. What would you have done if I hadn't called? Dropped little hints about the mystery woman in your life? I won't stand for being deliberately provoked like that, Logan Saber!"

"I didn't do it deliberately," he told her coolly. "Maryann showed up unexpectedly yesterday afternoon on her way to Hawaii. And while I didn't set up the situation I'm not sorry that it happened. Now you know how I felt when I walked in the other morning and found Kevin Thorne in your kitchen!"

"That was different!" Hilary defended herself childishly.

"No, it was not. Now calm down and tell me that you're missing me. That I'm not spending sixteen hours a day trying to get things in shape so that I can take time off for our honeymoon for nothing!"

"Are you?" she asked involuntarily.

"Spending sixteen hours a day on business? Yes, I am," he told her deliberately. "Tomorrow I shall spend the entire day tied up in meetings!"

"On Saturday?"

"On Saturday!"

"I see. Well, you must do as you see fit, of course, but you know we don't have to rush into marriage. We could put things off for a couple of weeks, get to know each other. Logan we have a lot to talk about . . ." Hilary rambled helplessly.

"Forget it, I'm not putting off our marriage one minute longer than is absolutely necessary. What's more, you'd be very disappointed if I did!" The phone crashed down in Hilary's ear and she could almost feel his temper sizzling along the line. He hadn't even waited until she could tell him that she missed him!

The idea was in Hilary's mind from the moment she awoke the next morning. It was a ridiculous, crazy thing to do but the more she thought about it, the more appealing it became. Logan would be so surprised, she told herself with an inner smile. It would mean missing the lunch time crowd at the Silver Salt Cellar, but the staff could handle it. She would be back in plenty of time for dinner.

With a growing sense of excitement, Hilary selected a salt cellar from her collection, a delicate, crystal thing with beautiful fluting around the edges, wrapped it carefully and picked up the phone.

A few minutes later she jumped into her car, heading for the airport. The commuter flight left in half an hour and she would have a very short time in Los Angeles to accomplish her goal and still make the return trip. It was an expensive, foolishly romantic project but perhaps that was the source of its appeal, she thought happily.

At the airport in Los Angeles she caught a cab to Logan's office building, fretting the entire route about what she would do if the building were closed. But it wasn't. With a glowing sense of excitement she took the elevator to the right floor, praying she wouldn't run into him in the hall. That would spoil everything. But he'd said he'd be tied up in meetings all day. Would his secretary be working overtime, too?

She was.

"Why, good morning, Miss Forrester!" E. Morgan exclaimed in surprise. "We weren't expecting you! At least, Mr. Saber didn't mention . . ."

"It's all right. I don't need to see him," Hilary assured her cheerfully. "I just wanted to leave this for him." She held out the package with the salt cellar inside. "Is he in his office?"

"No, he's out having a luncheon conference with . . ." E. Morgan explained anxiously.

"No problem," Hilary interrupted. "May I leave this on his desk?"

"Why, of course. Here, I'll let you in." The secretary rose quickly, leading the way to the inner office door. "Are you sure you don't want me to phone him? I have the number of the restaurant where he's lunching."

"No. Just give me a minute," Hilary smiled, walking into the silent office and picking up a piece of paper and pen from the huge desk. Quickly she jotted the note which read only, "I miss you" and left it with the package. She stepped back to the door, remembering her first time in the plush office and smiled.

"I have to be getting back to Santa Barbara," she explained on her way past E. Morgan's desk. "Nice to see you again."

"You came all the way from Santa Barbara just to leave the package?" E. Morgan said in astonishment.

"Yes," Hilary said, grinning, and left.

She was rounding the corner of the hall to the elevators when she heard Logan's voice. In a panic she scurried back a few yards and took refuge in the women's room. With the door opened a fraction she waited excitedly for him to pass. It would spoil the surprise if she announced her presence now but she couldn't resist getting a glimpse of him. Tomorrow he would be back in Santa Barbara, she reminded herself happily.

"Don't forget," Logan was saying as he strode briskly down the hall toward his office. "I want the contract you're drawing up for Forrester to sign to be explicitly clear. I don't want any ambiguity about the ownership of the restaurants."

"I understand, Mr. Saber," the other man responded as they moved past the door of the women's room. "There should be no trouble. You can obtain Mr. Forrester's signature tomorrow."

"Yes, I'll be seeing him. I'll take the paperwork with me to Santa Barbara. And another thing, Dave, will you . . ."

The voices faded as Logan and his companion disappeared into the office. For a moment Hilary stood transfixed, feeling like a fool for having let herself believe in Logan Saber, for making the ridiculous trip from Santa Barbara and for hiding in the women's room. It was all too much. Tears threatened as she found her way to the elevator where she stabbed the button in dismal fury. Why was it that every time she was beginning to trust the man something had to happen to prove her wrong? But the worst part was that she never seemed to learn!

Out on the sidewalk, Hilary managed to hail a cab for the airport, the ride back incredibly depressing. How could she have been so damn stupid? The man had exploited her weakness with no compunction whatsoever. Did he feel nothing at all for her? How could she fake that look of desire and need she had seen so many times in his eyes when they were together? How could he laugh with her one minute and make passionate love to her the next unless he felt something?

Was it possible that he did, indeed, feel a tenderness for her but was simply too good a businessman to give up the restaurants to prove it? After all, why shouldn't he have both if possible? It made excellent business sense!

By the time the plane landed in Santa Barbara, Hilary was a nervous wreck. It was all she could do to drive to the restaurant and put on the mask of a concerned, businesslike employer. Thank God for work, she told herself several times that evening as the crowd chattered around her. If she'd been forced to go home alone tonight she would have been in a pathetic heap on her bed. The demands of the Silver Salt Cellar were her salvation.

But even something as good as salvation must come to an end, she reflected sadly as she drove up the winding hill toward home. A long, lonely night stretched ahead of her. The moment she entered the house she removed the receiver from the cradle. She wanted no thank you calls from Logan Saber tonight! She didn't think she could deal with it and still remain rational.

What happened next, she wondered, undressing slowly and climbing into bed. Logan would no doubt arrive tomorrow morning as if nothing had changed. As it hadn't for him! It was only for herself that things looked different now. If only she hadn't overheard that conversation, she decided and then shook her head. No, better to know the truth. Fine. But what did one do with the truth when one didn't like it?

When she had heard Maryann's voice her reaction had been a jealous anger. But how did one berate a contract? Especially when she was one of the clauses! There were so few options and when Logan took her in

155

his arms, the options dwindled still further. If he suspected she was on the point of refusing to marry him again he would simply use the same tactics that had proven so effective.

And those tactics would leave her at his mercy once again. The reality of the situation was that she didn't want to back out of the marriage, Hilary forced herself to acknowledge miserably as she tossed and turned in bed. She knew she was clinging to a small straw of hope when she tried to tell herself that Logan did, indeed, have some strong feelings for her.

Far more likely that he found her an acceptable part of the deal Crawford was offering. Marriage to her was a term he was willing to meet. But if he was willing to tie her to him, didn't that imply that Logan saw her as something more than part of the deal?

Not necessarily, she thought sadly. He was a businessman. How could one trust a businessman?

For the first time in her ownership of the Silver Salt Cellar, Hilary seriously considered staying home from work the next morning. Only the knowledge that it would do absolutely no good finally convinced her to go in for the Sunday brunch. Every time the door opened to admit a new customer, Hilary started nervously. Soon it would open to admit Logan and her world would hover precariously on a dangerous brink in space.

When Logan did appear, however, she missed his entrance. She was busy in the kitchen, assisting the busy staff when someone pushed open the door long enough to tell her there was a man out front who wanted to say hello.

"He's gorgeous, too," she heard the waitress tell another member of the staff as she went slowly out into the dining room. "Just what Hillary needs. A good-looking, wealthy businessman!"

Hilary felt her ears turn red. She moved across the room with a growing sense of doom. The small smile plastered on her face was for the sake of the nearby customers and it took a lot of work to keep it in place.

She saw him before he saw her. Tall, self-assured and occupying the table for one with typical authority. If only he loved her, she thought wildly. She wouldn't begrudge him the restaurants if he truly loved her! But how would she ever know the truth about how he felt? Oh, in time, he would probably stop playing the game of seduction and then she would find out, but by then it would be much too late.

The idea hit her just before he turned and met her eyes. It was outlandish and possibly unworkable but if he agreed to it, she would have her answer. What she did with that answer was unguessable. But at least she would know how he felt about her. She had to know the truth!

"Hello, Hilary," Logan said softly as she neared. He got to his feet, his eyes going at once to the gold band around her wrist. There was satisfaction and possession in the gray-green eyes when they met hers again.

"Hello, Logan," she said equally softly, wondering how and when to make her proposal. It was going to take more courage than she had first thought.

He leaned down and kissed her lightly, showing a certain decorum at least in front of the customers. It was only as he was about to withdraw that he said outrageously in a whisper only she could hear,

"If you ever do that to me again, I swear I'll throttle you!"

"What!" she gasped, taking aback for an instant. "What in the world are you talking about, Logan?" She peered up at him, frowning in perplexity.

"I'm talking about the way you snuck into my office yesterday and left me the gift and the note," he told her huskily, pulling up a nearby chair and pushing her into it. "When I found out I'd just missed you it was all I could do to keep from braining poor Mrs. Morgan!"

"I wanted to surprise you," she said lamely, thinking about how excited she had been before she'd overheard that awful conversation with someone named Dave.

"The next time you take it into your head to do something so ridiculously romantic make sure you stick around to take the consequences, young lady," he ordered, eyes gleaming.

Hilary blinked and took a deep breath. "Well, speaking of romance," she began carefully, "I . . . I have something I want to talk to you about. . . ."

He waited expectantly and Hilary wondered precisely how one went about proposing a marriage in name only.

Chapter Nine

"I've been thinking about us," Hilary began determinedly, her gaze not quite meeting his.

"A bad beginning," he said humorously. "You shouldn't *think* about us, honey, you should concentrate on feeling . . ."

"Stop teasing me, Logan," she almost snapped. "This is important!"

"So I see," he retorted musingly. "But I have the impression I'm not going to like it. Well, let's get it over with. Or would you rather wait until you've closed the restaurant for the day?"

"Perhaps that would be best," Hilary found herself agreeing instantly, amazed at the sensation of relief she experienced. "I could meet you after I've finished here. Say about two o'clock. Where are you staying? Have you checked into your motel yet?"

"Funny you should mention that," he drawled. "Somehow, after finding the crystal salt cellar on my desk yesterday I was quite certain there would be a place for me in your home."

Unavoidably Hilary's lashes fluttered upward and she found herself confronting his very direct look. "Well," she began carefully, "That's one of the things I wanted to talk to you about. Please, Logan, I've got a lot to do here. You're right, it would be much better if we had this conversation later."

"All right," he sighed, looking vastly resigned. "Do you have any objection to my eating before I remove myself from the premises?"

"Of course not," she said quickly, getting to her feet. "I'll meet you at my place if that's okay with you?" She hovered nervously as he studied her anxious face and then nodded.

"Your place," he agreed. "Around two."

Hilary nodded and fled back to the kitchen where she found excuses not to emerge again until she was certain Logan had finished his meal and left.

This was utterly ridiculous, she thought angrily as she drove home after work. Her palms were damp with nervousness and her emotions seemed dangerously close to exhaustion. What was the matter with her? Logan was the one who was trying to trick her. *She* wasn't guilty of anything! Except the crime of putting him through another test, she reminded herself pointedly, parking the car and noting that a rental vehicle was already in the drive. Logan must have arrived.

"Hello, Hilary," he greeted her cheerfully, opening the door as she approached up the steps. "I heard your car . . ."

"One of these days you must tell me your secret with locks," she muttered.

"I can see you're in a charming mood. Tell you what. Go change into your jeans and we'll go down to the beach," he ordered, slapping her briskly on the rear as she went past him. The light blow didn't add to her uncertain frame of mind and she threw him a sharp

160

glare before hurrying off to the bedroom. But his only response was a small smile.

"Okay, let's have it," he commanded fifteen minutes later as he started the rental car and pulled into the street. "The suspense is killing me!"

"You don't look as if it's bothering you in the least," she observed morosely.

"Talk, Hilary."

"Logan, I . . . I have an idea." She flicked a quick sideways glance at his profile. "About our marriage."

"What sort of idea?" he prodded patiently.

"Well, we really haven't known each other very long and . . ."

"I've already told you I'm not going to postpone it," he reminded her swiftly, a hint of steel buried in the soft rumble of his voice.

"I'm not suggesting that," she said quickly.

"Good. What alternate little scheme has that churning brain come up with now?"

"I think it would be best if we went ahead and got married in . . . in name only," she got out in a frantic rush, not daring to look at him. She sat staring fixedly out the window, awaiting his reaction.

But instead of sounding either furious or agreeable, Logan's response was an utterly uncomprehending, "What on earth does that mean?"

"You know," she explained sharply. "A . . . a marriage of convenience. A business arrangement!"

"A business arrangement," he repeated, still sounding blank. "Hilary are you suggesting we get married but don't sleep together?"

"What's so unreasonable about that? I mean, it would give us time to get to know each other and . . ."

"Wait a minute," he growled softly. "This is another test, isn't it? I'm being sent into the arena again and this time I'm not quite sure I understand the point. If I

161

agree to your crazy idea I'll come off looking like I don't want you. If I refuse to go along with it then you'll claim I'm rushing you."

"It's not a test!" she exploded, swiveling in the seat to confront him. "I'm offering a perfectly reasonable solution to a complicated problem! I should think you'd be grateful."

"Grateful! For having to keep proving myself? What man would be grateful for that? Let me tell you, Hilary Forrester, when I finally do extract a full surrender from you, I'm going to demand payment for all you've put me through! And I'm going to take great pleasure in collecting!"

"Don't you dare threaten me! I'm offering you a way out of the game you're playing. The least you can do is show me the courtesy of being honest with me!"

"Now what the devil are you rambling on about?" Logan pulled the car into a parking lot, switched off the engine and turned in the seat to face her. In the confines of the car he seemed very large and menacing. The gray-green eyes were glittering with a dangerous expression that made Hilary wish she'd avoided the entire conversation. Very carefully she let one hand drift toward the door handle.

"I'm talking about the game you're playing to get Crawford's restaurants!" she managed bravely, lifting her chin defiantly.

"Those darn restaurants seem determined to haunt me," he grated, eyes narrowing thoughtfully. "But I can't believe you felt this way yesterday or you wouldn't have made the effort to go all the way to L.A. just to surprise me. So what happened, Hilary? The woman who left me that crystal salt dish was telling me something a lot different than what you're telling me now."

"Things are a little clearer now than they were yesterday."

"What made them clearer?" he demanded.

"I've had a chance to think . . ."

"Don't give me that," he snapped, rapidly and visibly losing his patience. It wasn't a commodity he seemed to have much of around her, Hilary thought anxiously. She let her fingers close around the door handle. "Tell me the truth. What happened to put this nutty idea in your head about a marriage of convenience?" He didn't move but somehow she felt quite intimidated.

"If you must know I heard you discussing the contract for the restaurants with someone named Dave!" she spit out furiously, amber eyes flickering with gold. He wanted the truth; he could have it!

"The contract!" he exclaimed, sounding astonished. "How did you . . ."

"I was hiding as you went down the hall from the elevator," she admitted on a quieter note. "I didn't want you to see me and spoil the surprise so I . . ."

"Hiding in the hall? How could you . . . ? Oh. The women's room, I suppose?"

Blushing, Hilary nodded mutely.

"My word," he shook his head disbelievingly, "if I'd known you were so close I'd . . ."

"You'd have been more careful about what you were discussing?" she supplied harshly.

"No, I'd have come in and yanked you out and introduced you to Dave. He's been very curious about you," Logan corrected with a hint of a smile.

"Why should he be curious about me? Or hasn't he met many women who let themselves be married for business reasons?"

"You've put him through a lot of work in the last few

days and there's more to come. But he's not altogether unhappy about it. He's looking forward to moving to Santa Barbara, too."

"What are you talking about?" Hilary exclaimed, baffled by the change in conversational topic.

"About moving to Santa Barbara, naturally. What else did you expect me to do?" he explained calmly.

"You're . . . you're moving here?" she yelped, totally astounded.

"I'm moving the business here. It will take some doing, but I'm looking forward to the challenge."

"I don't understand," she said a little humbly, trying to comprehend his meaning. "You're moving your entire firm to Santa Barbara? Just like that?"

"It's not that large," he smiled. "There's no reason things can't be managed from here as well as they were in Los Angeles. Not all the staff is coming. Some have their homes in L.A. but I'll be maintaining a branch office there for some time so no one's going to lose their job. Did you think I was going to spend my weekdays in the city and only see you on weekends?"

"Well, I . . . it was one of the things we had never talked about," she said quietly. "One of the reasons why it seemed like a good idea to get to know each other before we . . . you know," she broke off lamely, feeling more than a little overwhelmed. He was moving to Santa Barbara! Because of her? Or because the restaurants were important enough. . . . No, that didn't make sense. Nothing made much sense at the moment.

"Before I make you tell me how much you love me?" he finished for her, smiling at the red that swept in and out of her cheeks. "Hilary, you little idiot," he went on fondly. "When are you going to stop fighting me? Things will be so much easier when you admit the truth."

"The truth about how you're still after the restaurants?" she shot back, but her heart wasn't in it and it was obvious.

"The truth about how you feel. Look at you, an independent, intelligent, creative, successful businesswoman who's going to marry a man who might be after her for business reasons. Doesn't that tell you anything at all?"

"Only that I don't seem to be functioning at full capacity," she conceded grimly, staring out the car window at the ocean beyond.

"What about me?" he continued persuasively. "Here I am with pretty much the same qualifications as yourself about to marry a woman who's run me through the gauntlet! If you used your head for a minute you'd realize that no man in his right mind would put up with what I'm tolerating for the sake of a restaurant or two!"

She flashed a quick look at him before returning her gaze to the ocean view. "How do I know that? You haven't seemed to be suffering very much. You make it sound as if I've made you march to the ends of the earth and back in order to prove yourself!"

"It feels like it," he grinned outrageously.

"Well, it didn't do much good, did it? I still don't have my proof!"

"Not because of any failure on my part!"

"You're impossible, utterly impossible, do you know that?" she muttered ruefully.

"Sometimes I feel the same way about you, sweetheart. But I have confidence everything will work out in the end. Come on, let's go for a walk on the sand. My city feet have been looking forward to this for the past two days!" He opened the car door and climbed out, leaving Hilary with little option but to follow slowly.

"Logan?" she said softly as he came around to take her hand and lead her toward the water's edge. "About my . . . my suggestion. . . ." She turned a serious, almost pleading pair of amber eyes on him but he only smiled gently and kissed the crown of her braids. "A marriage in name only . . ."

"Let's forget your little suggestion," he said kindly and hauled her along behind him as he started forward toward the sand.

It wasn't until they reached the foaming edge of the sea that Hilary allowed herself to admit Logan had passed his latest test. He might want the restaurants, she told herself bracingly as she strolled along beside him, but he seemed to want her, too. Surely that was a hopeful sign?

For the rest of the afternoon, Hilary refused to allow herself to think of the business implications of her forthcoming marriage. Instead, she threw herself into showing Logan around Santa Barbara. They toured the lovely old Spanish mission with its quiet, cool cloisters and gardens, took the scenic drive that wound through elegant estates and had coffee overlooking the marina.

"I vote for eating at home tonight," Logan said toward the end of the day. "What do you say we pick up some steaks and barbeque them out on the veranda?"

Hilary nodded, thinking that he'd used the term home unconsciously. Was he thinking of it that way? There was something warming about hearing a man mention the word home like that.

Logan pitched in, doing his share in the kitchen and proving quite efficient.

"One of the advantages of marrying a long-time bachelor," he told Hilary when she complimented him at one point. "I'm already housebroken."

She smiled at him, setting the plates on the table. "Why haven't you married before now, Logan?"

"Too busy, I guess," he said easily, helping himself to the salad he had made. "That plus the fact that the right woman had never come along. The same reasons you haven't married, I imagine."

"But you're not too busy now?" she pressed, cutting into the rare steak and using the action as an excuse not to look directly at him.

"Let's just say my goals have changed slightly," he smiled. "Remember that conversation we had about the Crisis of the Thirties? Well, I've decided I want a few other things out of life besides an empire. In fact . . ." He paused so long Hilary was forced to glance up.

She found him waiting for her attention with a serious, thoughtful look in his eyes. "In fact what, Logan?"

"How would you react if I told you I would like to, umm, divest myself of a few of the accountrements of an empire?"

She chuckled slightly. "Big words. What are you saying?"

"That I'd like to run a little smaller business," he said flatly, sounding vaguely uncertain. "Spend more time on other things . . ."

"You want to sell what you've built?" she asked curiously, tilting her neat head to one side and studying him carefully.

"Not all of it. Just bring it down to a less troublesome size. We'd never go hungry, honey, but we might not have all the luxuries we could have if I kept on at my present pace." Logan set his fork down on the table and faced her. "What do you think?"

"I think," she smiled softly, "That sounds like an excellent solution to your crisis."

"Are you sure, Hilary?" he prodded, searching her face.

"Of course, I'm sure," she told him, her smile widening. "Life is too short to spend it doing nothing but making money. Why do you look so surprised? How did you expect me to feel?"

"More businesslike!"

"You keep telling me us business types have hidden depths," she laughed.

"Yes," he nodded and then smiled into her eyes. "Thank you, Hilary."

"For what?" she asked, confused.

"For wanting me more than you want my money."

"Did you think the reason I had agreed to marry you was because you were wealthy?" she asked, shocked. His money had never been a factor and it was startling to imagine he might have thought otherwise.

"Not really, but it's comforting to hear you confirm it."

"I suppose you think you're entitled to a test or two of your own?" she said a bit sharply, not liking the notion that he had doubted her. Was that how he felt when she expressed her doubts about him? It was a sobering idea. "I thought you were quite sure of me?"

"I won't be completely sure of you until you're all mine," he said deliberately, his expression leaving no doubt of his meaning. "For a man there is no other way to know with certainty that a woman is truly his. I need the reassurance of your surrender, little one."

"And what do I get out of it? Surrender doesn't sound like a very viable option for the one doing the surrendering!" Hilary said waspishly, feeling herself redden again and refusing to meet his eyes.

"If anything the risk I'm running will be greater than yours," he countered wryly.

"What are you talking about?"

"I'm talking about the power you have over me. And once I've made you mine, that power will increase. Neither one of us can keep our emotional distance from each other. This isn't going to be an affair, Hilary, this is going to be a marriage. In our case that will mean something!"

Hilary brought her gaze up to his once more, surprised by the intensity of his words. The warmth and flame which flickered lambently in the gray-green eyes was startling. It brought forth an answering response in her own feelings that threatened to engulf her. But before she could find some sort of verbal response, Logan was going on to another topic.

"I'll have to go back to L.A. tomorrow," he said more prosaically. "I've arranged for the marriage to take place on Wednesday morning. I'll be arriving back in Santa Barbara about an hour before the ceremony. Your father will take you to the church and I'll meet you there. I think all the details have been taken care of, although you and I will have to go through the legal work tomorrow morning before I leave," he added thoughtfully.

Hilary said nothing, rising to clear away some of the dishes. He had it all neatly tied up, she thought.

"You'll make arrangements to be away from the restaurant for a week or so?" he inquired, watching her make her way indoors with the dishes.

"Yes, I can manage that," she agreed quietly. "Where are we going to spend the week?"

"I thought we might drive up the coast. Take our time and stop where and when we feel like it. It will still be quiet along Highway One this time of year. The tourists won't be out just yet. How does that sound?"

"Fine," she whispered.

"Hilary?" he said from behind her, following her into the kitchen.

"Yes, Logan?"

"It will be all right, sweetheart. I promise you."

"I hope so," she breathed. "Everything's happening so fast . . ."

"Because I can't wait for you, Hilary honey. You're much too important to me. Don't you know that yet?" He removed the plates from her hands and pulled her into his arms. "I need you so badly." He molded her against him and this time she didn't try to resist. What was the point? He would only overcome her efforts in the end and deep down she wanted him as much as he seemed to want her. Hadn't he already made her admit that much?

But this embrace wasn't the raging, demanding thing the others had been. His kiss was gentle, lingering, savoring. And when he pulled back, she was hungry for more.

"Do you play cards?" he asked unexpectedly, humor in his expression.

"Not very well," she told him honestly, a bit confused. Why was he talking of cards when she had shown no resistance to his lovemaking?

"Good, neither do I," he grinned. "What do you say we put some music on that expensive stereo system of yours, pour some brandy and relax. We've both had a busy week. I think we deserve it."

"All right," she agreed, eyeing him curiously. Together they hurried through the rest of the dishes and then Logan poured the brandy while she selected some old French harpsichord music for the stereo.

It was as if they had agreed on a fragile sort of truce for the evening, she decided, accepting her brandy snifter and sitting down beside Logan on the couch. Neither of them had brought up the subject of where he was to spend the night and she didn't have the courage to bring it out in the open just yet. It was too pleasant just being with him in a quiet way. She smiled as Logan sighed and stretched out his long legs on the hassock.

"Were you really putting in sixteen hour days while you were in L.A.?" she asked lightly as he reached out to turn down the lights.

"Scout's honor!" he grinned, settling back and putting his arm comfortably around her shoulders, drawing her close. "And I'll be spending more of the same until I leave Wednesday morning. There's a lot to square away before I make my big lifestyle change!"

"You're sure the change is what you want?" she asked a little anxiously. "You're accustomed to a much more high-powered world than you'll find here in Santa Barbara. Won't you miss the big city?"

"Not in the least. The big city had begun to pall before I met you. You simply hastened the process. Brought everything into focus, so to speak. I know what I want, Hilary, don't worry."

Hilary thought briefly of the contract for the restaurants and then put it out of her mind. She would think of it tomorrow. Not tonight.

They sat quietly talking for some time after that, running through a variety of subjects which touched on just about everything except themselves.

"What time do you leave tomorrow?" Hilary finally asked when a glance at the clock showed that midnight was rapidly approaching. They had been talking for hours.

"Nine-thirty," he told her, promptly, removing his arm and stifling a huge yawn. "Which makes me think we'd better get to bed." He stood up, pulling her to her feet beside him.

Now that the moment was upon her, Hilary still couldn't bring herself to ask him point blank where he planned to spend the night. It was becoming fairly obvious he meant to stay with her, though, and she had a strong feeling she wasn't going to fight it. Under the quiet spell cast by the evening together it seemed pointless to try and refuse him her bed. He was going to be her husband shortly and even if she wasn't altogether certain of what he felt for her the thought of spending the night in his arms was far from unappealing. There was magic in the air when she and Logan came together. It would make her forget for the time being about the reasons for their marriage.

"You go on and get ready for bed," he instructed softly, turning her about by the shoulders and giving her a push toward the bedroom. "I'll get my things from the car."

With a last glance at him, Hilary did as she was told. Tonight it seemed easiest to let him take the lead. With a growing sense of anticipation, Hilary undressed and climbed into bed. She lay in the darkness, listening to him come back into the house and rustle around for a while. Why was he waiting, she wondered?

When she heard the springs of the hide-a-bed couch protesting squeakily she realized Logan had no intention of spending the night in her bed. He was going to spend it in her living room!

With an unexpected rush of dissatisfaction, Hilary sat straight up in bed, about to throw back the covers and march into the living room, demanding an explanation. Then with a groan of rueful confusion, she settled back down. Oh, that man! she thought, not for the first time. Would he never cease doing the unexpected? She wasn't sure her nerves could survive his strange brand of campaigning in a war she was rapidly finding excuses not to fight.

Chapter Ten

Logan woke Hilary with a glass of orange juice early Monday morning. It was the second time she'd had the experience of waking in his presence and this time she was determined to be nonchalant about the whole thing. Not for the world was she going to let on that she would have let him spend the night in her bed with very little urging! Two could play at the business of being cool, she had decided before finally falling asleep several hours earlier.

"What? No red roses this morning?" she managed to quip, sitting up and blinking sleepily.

"I don't want you to form any bad habits," he smiled, setting the juice down on the table beside her bed.

"Like expecting roses strewn on my bed every morning?"

"Like knowing what I'm going to do next," he retorted smoothly standing over her and drinking in the sight of her with the honey braids falling across curving shoulders.

"What perverse satisfaction can you derive from keeping me constantly off balance?" she grumbled, reaching gratefully for the orange juice.

"My male ego feeds on such things," he confessed with a low laugh.

"You won't be able to keep it up forever, you know," she warned, slanting a glance upward as she sipped the juice.

"I don't intend to try. At least not as constantly as I've been doing it lately," he said easily, hands on his hips as he watched her, an avid expression flaring deep in his eyes.

"You mean you're going to let up eventually? I don't believe it!" she exclaimed drily. "What will I have to do to deserve it?"

"Love me," he said with such unexpected roughness that she jumped a little, jarring the glass. "Completely and without any reservations," he clarified in case she hadn't understood.

But Hilary knew what he was talking about and in the invigorating light of morning she felt a resurgence of the spirit that had been sadly missing the previous night.

"You're talking about surrender again," she snapped. "You might have had a more positive response to your courtship if you'd been a bit less demanding . . ."

"Don't talk to me about demanding after I just spent a night on your couch," he cautioned with such feeling she eyed him warily. "I was a model of restraint last night!"

"Well, don't blame me for that," Hilary responded before she could think. "I never said you had to sleep there!" Instantly she wished she could have bitten her tongue. Her eyes flew to his.

"That's quite true," he agreed politely.

"You could have gone to a motel," she hastened to add firmly.

"Or I could have shared your bed."

"Not necessarily," she retorted loftily.

"Want to bet?" he smiled wickedly, leaning over her in what she could only describe as an intimidating fashion.

"Yes," she declared roundly, edging with apparent unconcern to the other side of the bed. "You're not going to have everything your own way, Logan Saber. . . . Mmmph!" she yelped as he caught her before she could get to her feet.

With a swift movement he yanked her gently back into the bedclothes until she sprawled helplessly beneath his gaze. Seeing the devil dancing in the gray-green eyes she began struggling instantly.

"Let me go," she insisted with as much fierceness as she could muster under the circumstances.

"Not until you admit that I could have spent the night here in your bed without much protest from you!"

"Logan, this is ridiculous. You have a plane to catch and you said yourself we have to get the license . . ."

"At the moment I happen to find this much more important," he drawled, holding her still. "Now tell me the truth my sweet battlemaid or I'll climb into bed with you and force the words out of your mouth."

He was fully prepared to carry out his threat, Hilary realized as she stared up at him. And the last thing she wanted this morning was to have him wring a confession of love from her and then take off for Los Angeles! Better to pacify the ruffled mood of her big jungle cat . . .

"Whatever you say," she got out ungraciously.

"That's not good enough."

"All right," she grated. "Maybe you could have spent the night here. We'll never know, will we, because you didn't choose to try?"

"Do you know why I didn't make the attempt?" he asked in a suddenly gritty growl.

"Why?" she heard herself ask involuntarily, watching him with wide eyes.

"Because you didn't ask me nicely," he grinned, releasing her. "Now hurry up and get dressed. We've got a lot to do." He turned and strolled out of the room.

Because she hadn't asked him nicely! Hilary repeated his words in dumbfounded silence as she scurried through the morning's routine. Since when had Logan Saber ever waited to be asked? One of these days she was going to turn the tables on that man, she vowed as she pinned her braids in place.

A couple of hours later Logan was gone leaving Hilary alone to face the short time before her wedding. His absence left her feeling decidedly restless and uncertain and with the restaurant closed there was nothing to take her mind off her swirling thoughts. In the afternoon Hilary got in the car and drove down to the beach, searching for a quiet spot where she could think.

She found it eventually, a rocky area where the breakers crashed a few feet away from an inviting seat on sun-warmed stone. What was she getting herself into, Hilary wondered, watching the waves and toying idly with a twig. In a very short time she would be marrying a man who's chief interest in her might very well be her dowry!

No, she told herself forcefully. The restaurants might have been the original reason for his interest but there was more between them now than a mere business deal. And hadn't Logan repeatedly denied the importance of the restaurants? Then why had he gone ahead with the contract between himself and Crawford? If only she hadn't known about that, Hilary thought dismally, tossing the twig to one side.

Still, she reminded herself, he was a businessman, even if he'd shown evidence of some wildly romantic depths. It was possible he could want her and simply saw no valid reason not to take the restaurants, too. It would be a logical move. What about his statement that he wanted to cut back his business interests, though?

Well, she thought miserably, it was all too confusing. Perhaps she should be concentrating on her own reactions and not trying to fathom Logan's actions. What did she, Hilary Forrester want?

And quite suddenly everything came sharply into focus.

Hilary sat staring a while longer, knowing she had the answer to her dilemma about the restaurants and knowing in a simultaneous chain of logic that she would never use it. It was simple really. All she had to do to satisfy the question of the restaurants was put Logan through one more test. She could demand that he sign a statement saying he would not go through with the contract to take over Crawford's businesses. Logan was a man of his word, she knew instinctively. If he signed such a statement, he would honor it.

But at the same moment that the idea for the latest test sprang into being, the knowledge that she would never ask him to go through with it was there. And with that knowledge, she had her ultimate answer. She loved Logan. Loved him to much to deny him the restaurants or herself.

Feeling as if a great weight had been lifted from her shoulders Hilary scrambled up from her seat on the rock and walked down to the water's edge, a smile on her lips and a sense of peace in her heart. She was in love. Wildly, romantically in love in a way that she had always thought was reserved for other women. Who would have guessed that she would find herself a man who understood the secret part of her? Logan could have all the restaurants he wanted as long as he wanted her, too!

Hilary seemed to be the only calm one as Wednesday morning approached. Her father was genuinely excited, escorting her to dinner Monday night and taking all the credit for having discovered Logan. Kevin Thorne and the staff of the Silver Salt Cellar held a surprise party for her after the restaurant closed for the day on Tuesday.

"I'd take you out to dinner tonight," Kevin grinned at one point as she opened gifts from her staff, "but I'm a little afraid to push my luck! I have an awful feeling Saber would break my neck if he found out."

Hilary laughed, examining the beautiful copper pan she had just unwrapped. "I'm going to be swamped, anyway, Kevin. But thanks for the thought." The gold manacle gleamed flatly in the light and she realized it was probably best that Kevin had decided to be cautious.

"You're going to make a perfect couple," Sheila the waitress announced with satisfaction. "I saw him the other morning at brunch and he looks just right for you. You'll have so much in common!"

More than you'll ever know, Hilary thought with a small smile, catching Kevin's eye and seeing an answering twinkle. Of all her friends so far only he had witnessed Logan's possessiveness.

Even though the wedding was to be a simple matter held in the minister's office it was surrounded with the usual bustle and confusion which seemed to accompany all weddings. While her staff and friends chattered excitedly and Crawford stood talking to a gorgeously dressed Julia, Hilary waited with a serene patience for Logan to arrive. She was sitting on the stone bench on the front lawn of the small church, discussing some last minute instructions with her chef when a car turned into the drive and Logan got out.

The gray-green eyes flew momentarily to Hilary and then, as if assured of her presence he walked around to the opposite side of the car and opened the door for an attractive, well-dressed young woman. The shade of mahogany in the woman's hair instantly identified her. This had to be Maryann.

"Hilary, I'd like you to meet my sister," Logan said and added to Maryann in a voice of quiet pride. "This is Hilary."

"How do you do," Maryann said enthusiastically, her tone warm and welcoming. "When Logan told me that he was getting married I dropped everything and made arrangements to be back in time. I wouldn't miss this for the world!" She surveyed Hilary's neat suit and hair and smiled with sisterly satisfaction. "I can see you're going to be just perfect for my brother. I'm so glad he had the sense to find himself a nice business-woman who will understand him!"

Involuntarily Hilary glanced at Logan, saw the laughter in his eyes and returned it. Then she smiled charmingly at his sister.

"Thank you, Maryann. I'm so glad you could come."

The wedding went off smoothly. There was a ring of hammered gold that so closely reflected the circlet on her wrist that Hilary knew Logan must have had it made. When he slipped it on her finger no one but she was aware of the almost savage flash of possession in his expression and the fierce grip on her hand. Yet his kiss at the end of the ceremony was uncannily gentle.

"Come on," he whispered grimly when they could finally get away, "Let's get out of here!" He led her through the small band of well-wishers, waited impatiently for Crawford to kiss his daughter goodbye and then bundled her into the car.

"And that," he announced with a grin as he pulled away from the curb, "Takes care of the legalities of ownership!"

"Logan!" she protested laughingly, "What am I going to do with you? Never have I met such an out and out chauvinist!"

"I'm sure you'll find a way to handle me," he declared imperturbably.

They drove for miles along the coast, sometimes talking, sometimes enjoying a companionable silence. But always Hilary was aware of the approaching night and her decision to tell Logan of her love. It would be her wedding gift to him and there would be no need for him to wring the words out of her. Between them now flared a kind of expectant energy that was evidenced in a multitude of small, meaningful ways. A glance, a touch, a smile. The undercurrent was subtle and deep.

Logan eventually stopped for the night at a small, secluded resort on the rocky coast.

"This place had better live up to its billing," he said after they'd checked in and been shown to the room. He dismissed the bellboy and flung open the door with a flourish.

"Oh, my goodness!" Hilary exclaimed, overwhelmed. She stood for a moment, surveying the sheer, unadulterated romance of the room with its wall to wall view of an isolated section of ocean, the unabashedly sensuous decor and the champagne which waited in a silver ice bucket. On one side was a fireplace and in front of it . . .

"Is it real?" she murmured, entranced by the huge, richly piled bearskin rug.

"It better be," Logan chuckled from behind her. "It

was the desk clerk's description of the bear in front of the fire which sold me on the place!"

Hilary turned to him, laughing delightedly up into his face. "I have a feeling no one at the wedding could begin to guess the kind of environment you've provided for tonight!"

"Just as they couldn't begin to guess what exists between us," he said softly, caressingly.

"Yes," She agreed simply, making no effort to deny it.

They dined in an elegant setting and afterward Logan led Hilary out onto the dance floor where she went willingly into his arms. He held her close, moving her sedately around the room and then said quite calmly into her ear,

"Do you want to take odds on how many dances I can get through before I succumb and drag you back to that bearskin rug?"

Hilary felt the warm flush rise into her cheeks and buried her face in his shoulder. "Hush," she begged, "Someone will hear you!" But she couldn't deny the thrill that went through her and Logan's low rumble of laughter told her he was aware of her feelings.

In fact, he only made it through one dance. At the end of it he looked searchingly down into her face and said quite simply,

"I want my wife." Without a word he turned and guided her through the crowd, back down the hall to their opulent room and escorted her inside. Hilary made no protest although the excitement hammered at her heart. She had to tell him. She wanted it to be before he had made her his in every sense of the word.

"Give me a moment or two?" she begged softly, her amber eyes vibrant and heavy with gold.

"Only a moment," he conceded. "I can't wait much longer."

Without a word she swept up her small overnight case and hurried into the bathroom. There, in privacy, she took down her hair, letting it hang in a rich cascade and slipped into the satiny nightgown she had bought the day before. Aware of the heat in her cheeks but totally unaware of the warmth in her eyes, she emerged cautiously from the bathroom to find the romantic bedroom lit only by the light of a flickering fire. In front of it Logan lounged on the bearskin rug, a glass of champagne in his hand. He was still dressed but the quiet tie had been removed and the white shirt unbuttoned halfway down his chest. He turned to look up at her as she walked toward him, the lacy gown floating around her ankles. Without a word he handed her a glass of champagne and tugged her gently down beside him.

"Logan," she began softly, a little uncertain how to say it. "I have something to tell you . . ."

"Do we need to talk just now?" he asked, one hand going to the wealth of honey-colored hair, his eyes glowing.

"Yes," she said in a whisper. "Logan I love you."

He met her eyes in a swift, surprised look.

"You love me?" he repeated, sounding almost dazed. "When did you come to that conclusion?" His fingers buried themselves in her hair.

"I don't know," she replied honestly. "I think it was there all along, but I finally acknowledged it after you left on Monday." She reclined on the rug beside him, her fingers tracing the hard line of his profile.

"You're sure?" he pressed, his hold tightening and the gray-green eyes beginning to blaze.

"Very sure." She smiled up at him, making no effort to resist.

"Tell me you're mine," he commanded, leaning over her on the thick, pagan rug. "Completely mine!"

182

The flames of the fire flickered on the gold of her bracelet as Hilary wrapped her arms around his neck and smiled invitingly up at him. "I'm yours, Logan. Can't you see? There is no one else except you. You are the only man in the whole world for me. The only one who understands me and the only one I love."

"Oh, my sweet Hilary," he breathed, his mouth crushing hers in a kiss that spanned the spectrum of love from desire to caring to possession. And she responded with uninhibited joyousness, arching her body against the caress of his strong hand, reveling in the feel and warmth and uncompromising masculinity of him.

"Hilary," he growled in his deepest lion's purr, "I want you so badly, my little pagan queen. I'll give you everything I have if you'll love me!" In a moment he was out of his clothes, settling down beside her again and pulling her close.

"I only want you," she said on a breath of sound as his hands pushed beneath the fragile covering of her night clothes. He touched her breasts in light, stroking movements that made her shiver and brought a low, passionate moan to her lips. She let her fingertips toy with the curling hairs of his chest and then wrapped her arms around him again as he swept her even closer.

"You shall have me," he swore softly. "As much as I shall have you. Completely. There can't be any other way between us, my beautiful Hilary. I've known that from the beginning!" He tugged at the nightgown, grew impatient when the small ribbons refused to unwind immediately and put his hand to the low vee opening in front. With a savagery belied by the heated love in his eyes he ripped the delicate material down the center until it fell away.

"Ah, sweetheart," he groaned, running his hand down the naked length of her as she lay on the barbaric

183

splendor of the bearskin. "I don't know how I managed to wait this long!" His eyes raked the sight of her from the fanned out honey hair, down the curve of breast and thigh, to the tips of her toes.

Hilary felt the flicker of flames on her skin and wasn't certain whether the heat was from the fire on the hearth or the blaze in his eyes. Both seemed to blend together as he explored her with a passionate mouth and possessive hands.

"Love me," she begged, lashes fluttering shut as she trembled with a need only he could fill. "Please love me, Logan!" Was this what he had meant by surrender? This incredible desire to love and be loved by only him? If so, then she gave herself into his keeping with total willingness.

There were no more words from him as he moved with a hungry, desperate intensity to make her his. The heat and longing and love he had generated in her seemed to further inflame the same emotions in him.

There was no gentle, teasing subtlety in their first encounter. Just as Hilary had known instinctively there would be, the emotions that flared between them were too raw and basic for the refinement of more civilized lovemaking. That could come later when they had time to learn each other more thoroughly.

She knew that a primitive, masculine need was driving Logan now as he crushed her beneath his hard length, his knee forcing her legs almost roughly apart although she had no thought of resistance. His elemental passions touched a responsive chord within her and she began to struggle, fighting him for the embrace in a fierce effort that forced him to hold her still as, with a groan of triumph and desire and need he made his possession of her a reality in the most elemental way there is between a man and a woman.

Hilary gasped as he became one with her, a small cry

of desire as primitive as his own escaping her lips. His hand still anchored her wrists above her head in the grip he had used to keep her writhing body still long enough to complete the union and she shuddered as he moved, guiding them both down a stormy, passionate path that was as old as time and as mysterious as tomorrow. It's end was a glorious revelation that Hilary knew the two of them would seek again and again together, a fiery, intoxicating delight that involved only herself and Logan.

"My sweet, passionate princess," Logan murmured a long time later as they lay entwined in each other's arms, recovering in a languorous fashion from the demands of their love. "I was so certain it would be like this between us . . ."

"How did you know?" she teased, a smile curving her mouth as she twisted slightly to look up at him where he inclined beside her, propped on one elbow.

"I knew the day you walked into my office and announced yourself as my future wife," he told her, an answering smile in his eyes. "As soon as I saw you I knew you were exactly what my wife would be like. Cool and businesslike to the world with only a hint of the passion inside . . ."

"What hint?" she chuckled, remembering her trim suit and neatly braided hair.

"Lots of little things. The way you wore your long hair in a manner that dared a man to take it down . . . ." Logan lifted a lock of the soft honey and wrapped his fingers in it.

"I never meant . . . !" she protested.

"Yes you did," he corrected, with a flashing grin. "And then there was that blouse of very passionate red peeking out from under the polite little suit. I'll never forget the way you sat in my office and told me you had no intention of marrying candidate number four!

185

Didn't you know you were throwing down the glove? Defying me to pick it up? I could hardly believe you weren't married already and locked away in some man's castle. I realized I couldn't waste a minute so I phoned Crawford up the second you had left. Told him I'd be delighted to take him up on his offer of a few days at his place in Santa Barbara."

"Did he . . . did he ever mention me directly?" Hilary asked curiously. Not that it mattered any longer, she told herself.

"Yes, at one point, he did," Logan admitted calmly. "I told him to go to hell with his idea of throwing in the restaurants as a dowry." He met Hilary's eyes evenly and she smiled.

"It doesn't matter, Logan," she told him sincerely. "There's no reason in the world you shouldn't have the restaurants. I'm glad to be able to bring you something as a wedding gift," she added fiercely.

"You're all the wedding gift I need or could handle," he growled, "Which reminds me, I have a little present for you . . ." He moved, getting lithely to his feet and walking across the room in gloriously unself-conscious nakedness. He rummaged in a bag and then came back to the rug, a gift-wrapped box in his hand.

She took it happily, pleased at his thoughtfulness. She busied herself with the ribbons, saying lightly, "Do you know what made me realize on Monday that I loved you?"

"Tell me!" he commanded with eager roughness, watching her fingers.

"I thought of one last trial for you and decided I couldn't put you through it!"

"What was that?" he asked curiously, putting out a hand to play with the tendrils of hair falling around her cheek. His eyes gleamed as he drank in the sight of her sitting nude on the bearskin rug.

186

"I had a silly thought to ask you to sign a contract with me saying you wouldn't accept the restaurants from Crawford," she said honestly, about to lift the box lid. She raised her eyes to his. "But I couldn't do it. I couldn't risk putting you through any more tests. When I realized that, I realized I loved you."

"Thank you, Hilary," he smiled. "But it wouldn't have made any difference. I told you once nothing you could do would drive me away from you!" He indicated the half-forgotten box in her hand. "Open it!"

"Yes," she agreed quickly, raising the lid and lifting the tissue. "What?" she asked uncomprehendingly, drawing out a folded piece of official looking paper.

"Read it," he ordered encouragingly.

Obediently she glanced at the document. "It's the contract between you and Crawford," she said wonderingly and looked up at him quickly. "Thank you for being honest about it with me, Logan, but it really doesn't matter any more. You can have all the restaurants you want . . ."

"Will you kindly shut up and read the thing, you little idiot?" he laughed.

"Well, all right . . ." Hilary bent over the paper, her eyes racing over the legal wording revealed in the firelight. As she read a small exclamation escaped her. "But this . . ." she glanced up again. "Logan this is a contract saying you'll never take the restaurants!"

"The contract you overheard me having Dave draw up when you were hiding in the women's room," he explained softly.

"Which should teach me a lesson about hiding in women's rooms," Hilary said wryly. "Oh, Logan, I'm sorry I ever doubted you. Can you forgive me?" she begged, watching him through her lashes.

"There is nothing to forgive," he whispered in a love-roughened voice. "Do you know, until I met you I didn't realize what was missing from my life. But when I saw you that first day it all clicked into place. I had to have you. You were the only woman on earth who could understand both the public and the secret sides of me. Just as I could understand you. We belong together, you and I, Hilary honey."

"I know," she smiled brilliantly, enticingly. "Sometimes I think we're throwbacks to another era. Other times I realize how very twentieth-century we are. It's like living in two worlds at the same time with you. Who could ask for more out of life?"

"There is nothing more worth having," he growled, reaching for her. "I have my slave girl, my lover, my friend and my queen, all wrapped up in the same woman."

"And I have my knight, my lover, my friend and my king," she murmured, going blissfully into his arms.

"Speaking of business," he said in his lion's purr, his fingers at her throat.

"Were we?"

"Yes. Speaking of business," he continued determinedly, "there are some fine points in our marriage contract I would like to go over with you . . ."

"But of course, Mr. Saber," she smiled, her arms twining around his neck. "I'm always available to discuss business affairs with you."

"Good," he commended, pressing her back against the thick stuff of the bearskin, "What I have in mind is a long term arrangement . . ."

"The rest of our lives?"

"At the minimum."

"Where do I sign?" she whispered invitingly and then they got down to business.

Silhouette Romance

IT'S YOUR OWN SPECIAL TIME

Contemporary romances for today's women.
Each month, six very special love stories will be yours
from SILHOUETTE. Look for them wherever books are sold
or order now from the coupon below.

$1.50 each

Hampson	☐ 1 ☐ 4 ☐ 16 ☐ 27 ☐ 28 ☐ 52 ☐ 94	Browning	☐ 12 ☐ 38 ☐ 53 ☐ 73 ☐ 93
Stanford	☐ 6 ☐ 25 ☐ 35 ☐ 46 ☐ 58 ☐ 88	Michaels	☐ 15 ☐ 32 ☐ 61 ☐ 87
		John	☐ 17 ☐ 34 ☐ 57 ☐ 85
Hastings	☐ 13 ☐ 26	Beckman	☐ 8 ☐ 37 ☐ 54 ☐ 96
Vitek	☐ 33 ☐ 47 ☐ 84	Wisdom	☐ 49 ☐ 95
Wildman	☐ 29 ☐ 48	Halston	☐ 62 ☐ 83

☐ 5 Goforth	☐ 22 Stephens	☐ 50 Scott	☐ 81 Roberts
☐ 7 Lewis	☐ 23 Edwards	☐ 55 Ladame	☐ 82 Dailey
☐ 9 Wilson	☐ 24 Healy	☐ 56 Trent	☐ 86 Adams
☐ 10 Caine	☐ 30 Dixon	☐ 59 Vernon	☐ 89 James
☐ 11 Vernon	☐ 31 Halldorson	☐ 60 Hill	☐ 90 Major
☐ 14 Oliver	☐ 36 McKay	☐ 63 Brent	☐ 92 McKay
☐ 19 Thornton	☐ 39 Sinclair	☐ 71 Ripy	☐ 97 Clay
☐ 20 Fulford	☐ 43 Robb	☐ 76 Hardy	☐ 98 St. George
☐ 21 Richards	☐ 45 Carroll	☐ 78 Oliver	☐ 99 Camp

$1.75 each

Stanford	☐ 100 ☐ 112 ☐ 131	Browning	☐ 113 ☐ 142 ☐ 164 ☐ 172 ☐ 191
Hardy	☐ 101 ☐ 130 ☐ 184	Michaels	☐ 114 ☐ 146
Cork	☐ 103 ☐ 148 ☐ 188	Beckman	☐ 124 ☐ 154 ☐ 179
Vitek	☐ 104 ☐ 139 ☐ 157 ☐ 176	Roberts	☐ 127 ☐ 143 ☐ 163 ☐ 180 ☐ 199
Dailey	☐ 106 ☐ 118 ☐ 153 ☐ 177 ☐ 195	Trent	☐ 110 ☐ 161 ☐ 193
		Wisdom	☐ 132 ☐ 166
Bright	☐ 107 ☐ 125	Hunter	☐ 137 ☐ 167 ☐ 198
Hampson	☐ 108 ☐ 119 ☐ 128 ☐ 136	Scott	☐ 117 ☐ 169 ☐ 187
	☐ 147 ☐ 151 ☐ 155 ☐ 160	Sinclair	☐ 123 ☐ 174
	☐ 178 ☐ 185 ☐ 190 ☐ 196	John	☐ 115 ☐ 192

Silhouette **Romance**

15-Day Free Trial Offer
6 Silhouette Romances

6 Silhouette Romances, free for 15 days! We'll send you 6 new Silhouette Romances to keep for 15 days, absolutely free! If you decide not to keep them, send them back to us. You pay nothing.

Free Home Delivery. But if you enjoy them as much as we think you will, keep them by paying the invoice enclosed with your free trial shipment. We'll pay all shipping and handling charges. You get the convenience of Home Delivery and we pay the postage and handling charge each month.

Don't miss a copy. The Silhouette Book Club is the way to make sure you'll be able to receive every new romance we publish before they're sold out. There is no minimum number of books to buy and you can cancel at any time.

This offer expires August 31, 1983

Silhouette Book Club, Dept. SBY 17B
120 Brighton Road, Clifton, NJ 07012

Please send me 6 Silhouette Romances to keep for 15 days, absolutely free. I understand I am not obligated to join the Silhouette Book Club unless I decide to keep them.

NAME_____

ADDRESS_____

CITY_____ STATE_____ ZIP_____